They Lived Their Love

37

They Lived Their Love

LULU HATHAWAY

and

MARGARET HEPPE

Illustrated by Joseph W. Papin

FRIENDSHIP PRESS   NEW YORK

10-4-65

Scripture quoted in the text is from the Revised Standard
Version of the Bible, copyright 1946 and 1952

Second printing August 1965

Library of Congress Catalog Card Number: 65-11436

1355819

Contents

They Lived Their Love

1 A Queen's Scout

JIMMY SHARD

All was not well at 19 Amberley Drive. The taxi driver at the front door shook his head as he rang the bell a second time.

"Patti-Ann!" The driver recognized Jimmy Shard's voice. "For the last time, no! I will not lend you any money! You spent all your allowance on candy and junk! Well, as far as I'm concerned, you can just go without until you get your money next week!"

The driver smiled to himself and quietly pushed open the

unlocked door to step inside. Neither Jimmy, in his wheel-chair, nor Patti-Ann, standing in front of him, noticed his arrival.

"I feel sorry for the poor man that marries you, Patti-Ann," continued Jimmy, in a heavy, big-brother tone. "He'll starve because you spent all the grocery money for candy!"

Patti-Ann made a face at her brother. "He won't be as bad off as the girl you marry, old skinflint. She won't even see any grocery money!"

The taxi driver coughed noisily. He would have to start soon to drive through Toronto to Jimmy's school. There was a burst of laughter from both as they realized they had an audience. Then Patti-Ann flew into the dining room. "I'll get your books, Jimmy," she called. As she put them into his arms, Jimmy said brusquely, "You can take that quarter on my dresser. But remember, it's the last cent you'll get from me! Spendthrift!"

"Miser!" called his sister as she ran to get the promised money.

"Ready, Jimmy?" asked the driver. When Jimmy nodded, he pushed the wheelchair carefully through the door and down the walk to the waiting taxi. Even more carefully and very gently, he lifted the boy into the front seat, then pushed the wheelchair into the garage. Jimmy winced as his body, crippled by muscular dystrophy, settled into the seat, but he said nothing. In a very few minutes they were on their way to Sunnyview, Jimmy's school.

"Mr. Jones," asked the boy politely, "did you ever have a ten-year-old sister?"

"Can't say that I ever did, Jimmy. Why?" Mr. Jones tooted his horn at a car about to back out into the street.

"Then you don't know what an ordeal it is," Jimmy said, shaking his head. But as he glanced at his school books on the seat beside him, his face brightened. "Oh, good. Patti-Ann remembered to put in my scout book today."

"What are you working on now in scouting, Jimmy?" asked Mr. Jones.

"Oh, mostly I'm just trying to get my patrol busy on their badges. Some of the boys are downright lazy." Jimmy was very earnest. "They make all kinds of excuses. I know they could all make First Class, but. . . ." He shrugged his shoulders.

Mr. Jones glanced briefly at the scout beside him. Jimmy's uniform displayed many awards. A First Class Badge, the result of two year's hard work at varied projects, was sewn on his left sleeve. The All-Round Green Cord, signifying that Jimmy had earned several proficiency badges in addition to his First Class, was looped around his right shoulder. And on his right sleeve, proficiency badges were neatly arranged in rows.

"Well, when you get all the others working, what then, Jimmy?"

"Oh, I'll work on another badge, maybe." Jimmy's voice was vague, but his eyes brightened as he answered, and a tiny smile crept around his lips. He paused for a minute, then went on in a calm voice, "There's the junior choir concert next week. I'm chairman of that. And I have to give a talk on scouting at the P.T.A. meeting." Again the brief smile. "I had a really good idea at rehearsal."

Mr. Jones turned the taxi into the mainstream of city-bound traffic before he asked, "What was that?"

"Well, I thought I'd try for the Entertainer's Badge. Maybe I could combine my P.T.A. speech with a song."

"That sounds like a good idea," said his friend. "But don't you have enough badges now? Looks like quite a collection to me."

Jimmy glanced down at his sleeve, and again the secret little smile appeared. He didn't answer for some time, and when he did, it seemed as though he had changed the subject. "I'll be fourteen next year, you know."

Mr. Jones looked a little puzzled, but before he had time to wonder what was on Jimmy's mind, they had arrived at Sunnyview.

"Tell me the rest when I pick you up this afternoon," he suggested as he cautiously lifted Jimmy into the waiting wheel-chair. "Don't work too hard," he said, and he turned Jimmy over to the teacher. Then, as he slid under the wheel of his taxi, he mumbled, "Can't say that to many kids these days, but that Jimmy is a hustler for sure."

Scout days seemed to go so much faster than other days! There was always so much to do. And today Jimmy planned to talk with his scoutmaster about the Entertainer's Badge.

But first he wanted to work with some of the boys in his patrol. They must not get discouraged and give up!

So, at the noon scout meeting, Jimmy was demonstrating a new knot to a little Tenderfoot when the scoutmaster walked up behind him. Mr. Buesnel's eyes clouded for a moment as he watched Jimmy patiently forcing his fingers to complete the knots. Gently the man placed his hands on Jimmy's shoulders.

"Oh hello, Mr. Buesnel. I've been wanting to see you." Jimmy's voice was carefully controlled, but his eyes sparkled.

"What's on your mind?" smiled the scoutmaster.

"Oh, nothing really. I just thought—well, as long as I have to give that speech—" Jimmy hesitated for a second, and then continued with a rush. "Could I add a song or something and try for my Entertainer's Badge?"

"That's a good idea. What else are you planning?"

"Well, I don't know. I suppose I should have something to end it with, shouldn't I?"

"Yes, I think so. How about a couple of numbers on your chord organ?" suggested Mr. Buesnel.

Jimmy smiled. "That sounds swell. Write it down on the program, if you like. That would finish it up in good style." And he returned to concentrate on the Tenderfoot's effort to tie the knot.

Jimmy was very fond of Mr. Buesnel, always so helpful and interested. But it was to Ferguson Reid, the Queen's Scout, that he really opened his heart. When Fergie came to Jimmy's home for his regular Tuesday visit, he was surprised to find Jimmy in a serious mood, quite unusual for him.

"What's the matter, fella?"

Jimmy looked at his friend for a moment before he spoke. "Tell me the truth now, Fergie. Honestly, do you think I've got a chance to make Queen's Scout when I'm fourteen next year? I mean—" His eyes dropped to his useless legs. "I just don't know if I possibly could. But if I could, it would be really great, not only for me but for all the boys in my patrol."

There was a pause as Fergie struggled to find the right thing to say. Before he could reply, Jimmy continued. "You see, everyone in my troop has some kind of handicap, and sometimes they use that as an excuse. I used to feel that way, too, sometimes, but scouting helped me get over it. I found out I could do so many things anyway—" A look of determination crossed his face. "It would help the other boys and keep them in scouting if I got to be a Queen's Scout. They'd know they could do it, too!"

Fergie tilted his head questioningly as he asked, "Will you have time for so much extra work? You have choir practice and church every week—and, of course, school work. It takes an awful lot of time and hard work to finish the requirements for Queen's Scout."

Jimmy looked at his friend with confidence. "I can manage, if you'll help me," he begged.

Fergie's only answer was a gentle tug of the boy's hair.

And so they began to work toward this difficult goal. There

were so many more badges to be earned! But Jimmy's mother helped, too. She didn't know about the Queen's Scout goal, for Jimmy and Fergie had decided to keep that a secret. But she knew that Jimmy sometimes became discouraged. There were days when he had a great deal of pain. There were days when his hands just wouldn't work. And days when he needed more of her love and encouragement than usual. Each morning she came to his room to help him dress for school.

"I never have to wake you, do I, Jimmy?" she said cheerfully one morning. She saw him put down his Bible carefully as she came in. Jimmy didn't answer her directly, but his eyes looked over to the framed motto on his wall:

> "You must seek him in the morning
> If you want him through the day."[1]

And the understanding look that passed between them spoke of this as a secret they shared.

The Entertainer's Badge was first. The scouts of Jimmy's patrol were very proud of their leader as he sat in his wheelchair on the stage. First of all, he sang "All in the April Evening," and his voice was clear and true. Then, after the applause died down, he began his speech. Talking about scouting was not difficult for Jimmy because he believed every word of what he said. Finally, his two numbers on the chord organ rounded out the program, one of the year's best.

[1] "The Secret," by Ralph S. Cushman. From *Spiritual Hilltops*. Copyright Renewal 1960 by Ralph S. Cushman. Used by permission of Abingdon Press.

Jimmy's badges added up faster than he himself realized. Some of them were great fun, even though he often grew tired. Some of the new badges came almost by accident as Jimmy, busily helping another scout with his work, found that he, too, had earned the badge! And the months passed, full of activity in church and school.

One day, Jimmy was surprised to see Ferguson Reid rushing into the house without even ringing the bell.

"Got some news today," Fergie said with shining eyes.

"Something super must have happened to you all right," said Jimmy. "You look as though you'd found an oil well!"

"Not oil—gold! A gold badge. And not me, you!"

"What?" shouted Jimmy, not daring to believe that. . . .

"It's true. It's the Queen's Scout Badge and you are to get it right now, as soon as they can arrange the award ceremony! You don't have to wait until you're fourteen. You'll probably be the only boy ever to be a Queen's Scout at thirteen."

Days later, the Great Hall of the University of Toronto was jammed as Jimmy Shard was wheeled forward to receive the hard-earned award. As it was pinned on his uniform, with one accord the entire audience rose to its feet to honor him. Jimmy saw that his mother was crying, but he knew that mothers were sometimes funny about crying when they were happy. Even his father seemed to be sniffing, as though he had a cold.

As the people took their seats amid a thunder of applause, Jimmy turned to his dad. "It's nice of all the people to stand up for me. But how do they all know I am only thirteen?"

As a part of the publicity that followed his award, Jimmy was asked to tell boys and girls what he thought their goals in life should be. This is a part of what he wrote:

I think we should have three main goals in life. We should belong to a church and join in as many of its activities as possible. We should join the Boy Scouts or the Girl Guides, because in them we are taught to think for ourselves. We should get as much education as possible so that we can serve our country which needs educated people to fill the demands of the future.

Finally the excitement died down, and things went back to normal in the house on Amberley Drive. Jimmy had loved all the fuss made over him, but he was glad when it was over. Sometimes his legs hurt a lot, and it was hard to keep brave and smiling all the time. He was sure that never again would anything as wonderful as this happen to Jimmy Shard!

It was his father who brought him the biggest surprise of his life. There was great pride in Dad's smile one evening.

"How would you like to go to Ottawa, Jimmy?"

"Ottawa? What for?" asked Jimmy.

"To meet the Governor-General," answered his father. He was trying hard not to be excited.

"Governor-General Vanier? Me?" cried Jimmy in surprise. "Oh boy!" Then after a second of thinking about this new adventure, he asked with a grin, "How will I get there? Will Chicken-Patti push my wheelchair?"

"You call me that name once more, and I'll call you Jimsey! Yes, I will, right in front of everybody!" Patti-Ann's voice sounded angry, but her face showed as much excitement as her brother's.

"We have all been invited to fly to Ottawa to meet Governor-General Vanier because you are to be awarded the Cornwell Medal," said Mr. Shard proudly. "What do you think of that?"

What Jimmy thought of it was easy to see in the next few days. In fact, he thought of almost nothing else! The excitement of the trip was almost enough to make him forget his pain. But when the great day came, Jimmy called his mother to his room. He was almost in tears.

"Oh, Mother, I don't believe I can go!"

"Why, Jimmy! What's wrong?"

"My foot. It hurts so today, I can't put my shoe on. I can't go to Ottawa with one shoe off!"

It took quite a lot of persuading, but finally Mrs. Shard convinced her son that it was Jimmy who had been invited, not his shoes!

Government House in Ottawa was beautiful. Jimmy had never seen so much elegance. He was greeted by the Governor-General, and the reception room was crowded with distinguished people from all over Canada.

And there in that lovely room Jimmy heard the words of the citation: "This scout's high character and devotion to duty in spite of long suffering continues to be an example to all.

To James Carl Shard, we award the Cornwell Medal, the highest award given to any scout." And then the tall figure leaned over Jimmy's wheelchair and the fingers fastened on the medal, while the kindly voice of the Governor-General was saying, "Congratulations, Jimmy."

Jimmy's throat seemed to close completely but with difficulty he stammered his thanks. Then there was much applause, and everybody seemed to be talking at once. Later refreshments were served, and Jimmy found Madame Vanier at his side.

"How does it feel to wear the Cornwell Medal, Jimmy?"

"I can't believe it, Ma'am," said Jimmy politely. Then he burst out, "But I was so ashamed to have the Governor-General see me without my shoe!"

Madame Vanier smiled with understanding. "I think he knows how you feel, Jimmy. Didn't you know that he himself has an artificial leg? And lots of people have seen him without it!"

"Oh," said Jimmy, his eyes wide. "And he's the Governor-General!" Then smiling up at Madame Vanier, Jimmy closed his fingers slowly but tightly around the medal.

QUESTIONS

1. Look up muscular dystrophy in the encyclopedia at school. In the light of the report, tell why this story about Jimmy should be included in a book about "living your love."

2. Find out the requirements for a Queen's Scout or an Eagle Scout. Would you find them easy to earn, without a physical handicap?

2   *She Brought a School*

HEA SOOK LEE

"Daughter! Daughter!" Mother's usually calm voice was ringing with excitement. "Look what has come for you!" She held out a very important-looking letter to the attractive girl who was just coming home from school.

Hea Sook put down her books and carefully opened the letter. She tried to prepare herself for bad news. She knew she mustn't be too disappointed if— But as soon as she had read a few lines she threw her arms around her mother.

"Oh, Mother! I can go! They've accepted me! I can go to Ewha! I've passed the exams and I can register in the English department!"

Mother and daughter looked at each other speechless with delight. Ewha University—right here in Seoul! The largest women's college in the world. For years Mrs. Lee had dreamed of sending her daughter to Ewha. "You must do well in school, Daughter," she had said to a tiny Hea Sook, "so that when you are older you can go to Ewha." And later, when Hea Sook was in middle school, her mother had told her, "When you graduate from college you will be able to help our country. Korea has need of good leaders."

Now at last the proud moment had come. Mr. and Mrs. Lee stayed up late that evening making plans with Hea Sook.

"It is well that we have already started planning for your entrance fee," said Mrs. Lee with satisfaction. "Your father has been keeping the store open later hours in the village, and we have all been getting along without new clothes, so that our daughter may be suitably dressed."

"Oh, Mother, you need a new cheema and chogeri (skirt and overblouse) this winter. I can wear my high school uniform for a long time yet. Ewha doesn't require a uniform—just a dark skirt and jacket for special occasions. I won't need a formal Korean dress until I'm a senior."

"No, no," Mrs. Lee was as excited as her daughter. "You must have new clothes. We are counting on you to bring honor to our name. You must dress well, and you must work hard, so that you can find work in one of the schools—perhaps even a middle school in Seoul."

And so Hea Sook went to college filled with the hopes and dreams of her mother and father as well as her own. And she did do well, just as they had known she would. She was especially good in English and became very fond of her English teacher.

One day toward the middle of the year she stopped after class to speak to this teacher. "Miss Conrow," she said, "I have heard about the Enlightenment Group, the students who go out to work in the villages. Can you tell me more about this group?"

Dr. Conrow looked fondly at the earnest girl. "Many of our students are worried about our country, Hea Sook," she said kindly, "and they would like to help the villagers. The refugees from North Korea have had a very difficult time, for there is not enough land or enough food for so many."

"But what can girls do?" asked Hea Sook.

"Any work that needs to be done," answered the older woman firmly. "Some of them teach classes for the children and some teach health habits and better cooking to the adults. But others work in the fields, build wells—they even repair roads. There is so much to be done." Dr. Conrow sighed.

"May the girls go at any time?" asked Hea Sook. "And could I join the group now?"

Dr. Conrow smiled. "You must speak to Professor Yoon, the sponsor of the program, for all the details, my dear. But

I can tell you this much. The girls in the Enlightenment Group give up their weekends and their vacations to go to the villages. And before they may go, they must take a training course here at the University."

"Oh, I would like to take the training course so that I could go," said Hea Sook eagerly. "I will speak to Professor Yoon right away."

Soon after this, Hea Sook started attending the special Enlightenment meetings, and after that she spent some of her weekends in nearby villages. The pinched faces and ragged clothes of many of the children touched her heart. The older people spoke of the long hours of back-breaking work trying to grow food in the poor soil. The best potatoes they could grow in the rocky soil were no bigger than marbles. Only a few families had enough water and land to grow rice. Most of the people were sick from lack of proper food, but there were no doctors. Each short weekend, Hea Sook did what she could, and in the time of the Great Cold she spent twenty days of her winter vacation in a refugee settlement.

One day as she was teaching a group of children to read from a book she had brought, she missed one of the little girls.

"Where is Kim Mijah today?" she asked. "She was doing so well in reading. Why isn't she here?"

But the children didn't seem to know, and Kim Mijah did not come. Not that day nor the next. On the second day, Hea Sook set out right after school to find the girl's home, to see what had happened.

It wasn't hard to find, this rough shelter of only one room, with pounded earth walls and floor. As Hea Sook stood in the doorway she could see in the darkness a movement from what looked like a bundle of rags on the floor. As her eyes grew accustomed to the dim light she saw that it was Kim Mijah. From the corner of the hut a thin, worn old woman struggled to her feet and came to the doorway. She recognized the girl from Ewha and welcomed her.

"I'm sorry Kim Mijah hasn't been to school," she said, "but she hasn't had strength enough to walk there."

Hea Sook was all concern. "Is she sick? Shall I get some medicine?"

"Not sick like that," the mother shook her head. "The weather has been too cold, so I couldn't cut wood for charcoal."

Hea Sook was puzzled. "I don't understand. What has charcoal got to do with Kim Mijah?"

"I cut wood every day when I can," replied the mother. "I walk five miles to the city to sell the wood for charcoal. But this week it has been too cold. We have had nothing to eat for three days."

Hea Sook wrote excited letters to her parents about her work in the villages. When she could get home to visit them she talked of almost nothing else. Her family grew very concerned, even angry about this.

"How will you make a good marriage, if your skin is all dark and sunburned?" scolded her mother.

"Will you be wanted as an English teacher in a good city school if you spend all your time in the country?" questioned her father angrily. "How can you bring honor to the family, or earn any money, working in the villages?"

But in spite of their disapproval, Hea Sook continued to work in the villages. In her mind an idea was growing stronger and stronger—the idea that this was the work God was calling her to do.

When she was a senior she lived in the English Practice House with Miss Gloria Jameson, a missionary. As their friendship grew, Hea Sook told the older woman of her problem.

"I can't decide what I should do after graduation," she worried. "I want to earn a good salary and help my mother and father. They have sacrificed so much for me. But I can't leave my people in the villages. My family are all against the village work, and I would like their blessing. I don't know what to do!"

Shortly before graduation Hea Sook sat in the office of the president of the university. The time had come for her to make her decision.

"Hea Sook," said the kindly president, "your work in English has been excellent. It may be possible for you to get a position as an English teacher in one of the middle schools here in Seoul. Would you like that?"

Hea Sook looked troubled. "My parents would be delighted," she said slowly. "It is what they have always hoped for." There was a long pause. Then she leaned forward. "Oh, Dr. Kim, what shall I do? I want to please my parents. I hate to hurt them. But you see——" Another pause as Dr. Kim waited. "You see, I know that the need is so much greater in the villages. The people in the country need us so much more!"

"What would you like to do, then, Hea Sook?"

Instantly the girl's face shone with eagerness. "I have heard of a village, away up in the mountains, about 150 miles from here. There are only about thirteen houses, and there is another smaller village nearby. There is no school and the people —oh, Dr. Kim, the people are so poor! I think I could help them. I would like to go *there!*"

"What about your parents?"

There was a sad but determined expression on Hea Sook's face. "They will just have to understand that this is something I must do. I cannot deny God's call." She had made her decision.

And so, right after graduation, Hea Sook started off for the village of Tapdong-ri. From Seoul she took a train, changed to a bus through the steeper mountains, crossed on three ferries, and finally arrived at the tiny village almost hidden in the mountains.

There was no one to meet her. She left most of her bundles, her food and belongings, books and papers, beside the road and walked toward the house of the head man of the village. He had offered the larger room of his two-room house for the school. Another family would share their home for her living quarters.

On her way she saw two boys playing. One was holding a worn-out rubber shoe in his hand while he kicked a rag ball with his other foot. A little girl with a baby on her back was watching from the corner of the house.

"Hello," said Hea Sook cheerfully. "I'm the new teacher. My name is Miss Lee. What is yours?"

The larger boy looked at her for a long time, then ducked his head shyly as he answered, "Kim Young Tak." They walked on together. Her work had begun.

The next morning Hea Sook held her first class. Six children were waiting outside the room. Hea Sook began to unpack her books. Soon a few more children stopped to see what she was doing. Before long there were ten sitting on the floor of the small room. The next day, a few more. By the end of the week, there were twenty-three children enrolled in the school. Only half could study inside at one time, so Hea Sook taught the younger ones, while the older ones played outside or sat on grass mats, looking at books and trying to hear what the teacher was saying. Later in the day the older ones came inside to study.

Hea Sook soon found that reading was not the only thing the village children needed. The soil was worn out and the harvests were poor. If the people could grow better crops they would have better food. Hea Sook knew nothing about farming, but she knew how to find out. She wrote letters—letters to anyone who could help with growing, harvesting, selling, and preserving. The result of all these letters was a busy 4-H Club, learning about methods of feeding the village.

Then the parents began to take an interest in learning, too. One of the mothers was appointed to speak to the teacher about this. "We would like to read the pamphlets, too," she said shyly, "but we cannot come to the school in the daytime, for we must work in the fields."

"Then come at night," replied the young teacher quickly. "We can have classes here after the children leave."

And so the school took care of the parents as well as their children. They learned to read not stories but farm books and recipes. The classes studied cooking and canning, so the children could have better food. The room became impossibly crowded, and the villagers knew that something must be done.

"How can we get a real school?" they asked among themselves. They met with the head man to talk it over. Everyone agreed to work in turn, two days at a time. The women and children would carry stones for the foundation and mix the mud and cement. They got permission to cut trees for the framework. American and Korean friends offered to pay for the cement and sent a skilled carpenter to supervise the work. For the first time since they could remember, the villagers were happy and hopeful. Idleness had been replaced by busy planning and hard work; despair had been replaced by hope and faith in the future.

One day, the county agent and Professor Yoon visited the village and suggested that they plant mulberry trees, so that they could raise silkworms. With the help of the Enlightenment Group and a government loan, twenty-five thousand seedlings were provided. And the Kansong high school students agreed to come during their spring holiday to plant them. In only two years, the plants would mature enough to feed the silkworms.

Among the letters Hea Sook wrote were several to the students in the Enlightenment Program back at Ewha University. In them she spoke enthusiastically about her work and invited her friends to come and visit the village. One weekend early in May, a whole group arrived—the new president of the Enlightenment Group; a social work graduate who would stay on in Tapdong-ri as a second teacher; and several of Hea Sook's old friends from Ewha.

"How do you know so much, Hea Sook?" asked one of them.

"I don't," she replied with a laugh. "The children and their parents and I are all learning together."

The Enlightenment president took Hea Sook aside and told her that a new group had been formed at Ewha. Calling themselves the "Torch Group," these graduates, faculty members, and students had banded together to sponsor the Tapdong-ri project. She put an envelope into the young teacher's hands. "It isn't much," she said, "but we have pledged to raise this amount for you each month. We want to help as much as we can." Inside was 2,000 won (approximately $17, in United States currency).

"How wonderful!" exclaimed the astonished Hea Sook. "This will help more than you realize."

And so, almost overnight, Hea Sook's dreams were coming true. Suddenly the new school was completed. It had space for two classrooms, a library which was also the clinic, and a kitchen and bedroom for the teachers. The county governor came for the first time to this remote village for the school's dedication. In addition, there were many important visitors from Seoul, from Ewha University, from the city newspapers. The people of Tapdong-ri were very proud of themselves, of their happy children, of their beautiful new school. And as they looked affectionately at Hea Sook Lee, they said among themselves," She brought us a school, our Hea Sook Lee. We will make a better life."

QUESTIONS

1. In what ways was Hea Sook's work Christian?
2. Why do you think it was hard for Hea Sook to decide whether to work in Seoul or Tapdong-ri?

3   *A Bridge Is Built*

TOM CHANG

A small Chinese boy bowed solemnly before the statue of
Buddha. The slanting rays of the early morning sun peeked
through the open door of the small pagoda and outlined the
boy's outstretched arms, holding school books, tablet, brush,
and a bottle of ink. In a sweet, winning voice the boy said
with great politeness, "Honorable Sir, please care for these
worthless tools of learning. Keep them safe from harm until
I return." Then with a quick, comical bob of his head, for he

could spare no more time on elaborate bows, he slipped the school materials behind the statue and scampered out into the sunshine for a long day of play in the nearby hills.

"This is a fine idea," Chang Ton-Shun said aloud. "I should have thought of this before. It's much better than sitting in school all day, learning all the wise sayings of Confucius. I don't think anyone will see the books, back of the Lord Buddha." Then, with a merry grin, he shook his black hair from his forehead. "Anyway, he will never tell where I put them!"

All day long Ton-Shun played in the sun-drenched hills. He longed for his kite, but his mother would have noticed if he had taken that. He chased butterflies, ate his noon meal by the stream, slept awhile, and lay on his back watching cloud patterns in the sky. Then, when it was time for school to be out, he got up quickly and brushed the twigs and grass from his blue cotton uniform. He ran his fingers through his hair trying to comb and smooth it down to its usual glossiness. Then he tore off as fast as he could to the tiny spirit hut, bowed his thanks to the silent Buddha, took his books and tablet under his arm, and walked home.

This delightful escape from school was fun, so he repeated it several times in a row. But one day, when Ton-Shun came home, he knew there was trouble. Venerable Mr. Ling, the schoolmaster, had been to visit his home. Ton-Shun had been missed at school; Mr. Ling hoped that he had recovered from his sickness.

Grandmother, outwardly respectful, had the same kind of sparkling mischief in her eyes as Ton-Shun. "That Number Sixty-three," she sighed. "He is his father all over again."

"Honorable Mother-in-law," Ton-Shun's mother had an unusual note of firmness in her voice, "this unworthy child of mine must not be allowed to continue this. One day he must stand with our great Chinese scholars. I shall speak to him."

Grandmother had a very warm spot in her heart for her gay, laughing grandson. Named Ton-Shun, he had always been called "Number Sixty-three," because he had honored her sixty-third year by his birth. She knew his mother was right, but it was hard to be angry at Number Sixty-three.

However, Grandmother did not interfere when Ton-Shun was called to answer for his mischief before his mother.

"But, Mother," pleaded the boy, "let me transfer to the government school. In our classical school we learn only of the past. I want to know about the world today, Mother. Let me change, please. I won't stay away again." 1355819

Mother smoothed back the black, wiry hair from the small face that reminded her so much of his father's, and saw that the dancing eyes were sober and quiet, the laughing face set in earnest lines. Her gentle smile was her answer.

Once in the new school, Ton-Shun kept his promise. He learned quickly and willingly. He no longer wrote his name Chang Ton-Shun but in the Western manner, T. S. Chang. He learned a great deal about the countries of the world and longed to visit them.

"The United States is a very important country, Grandmother. Someday I shall go there and then I shall come back and tell everyone in China what the rest of the world is like."

But even young T. S. could not have guessed that his words would come true so soon. While he was still in school, he was chosen as one of the nine Boy Scouts from China to attend the International Jamboree in the United States.

That trip gave him a dream that was to shape his whole life. For of all the thousand exciting impressions that he received in the United States, one stood out especially vividly in his mind: in every community he visited, people were reading newspapers. In China, only the largest cities had newspapers, and only the wealthiest people could buy them.

"Everyone," T. S. told his family upon his return, "everyone in the United States, young and old, rich and poor, reads a newspaper. I'm going to start them here in China."

"And how will my son accomplish this miracle?" asked his mother mildly.

"I'll graduate from school and get a scholarship to Central University," T. S. replied firmly. "Then I'll go to the United States, and soon I'll have lots of money to come back and start a chain of newspapers all across our province."

In T. S.'s eyes, the country newspapers he would start were already selling on newsstands in every Chinese village. "And Mother, they will be like bridges—bridges of understanding. Everybody who reads them will learn to understand the nations and peoples of the world."

The first part of T. S.'s dream came true on schedule. In a few years he graduated with honors from school and was ready to take his entrance examination for Central University.

In the meantime, however, war had come to China. Instead of walking across a campus with books and brushes, T. S. found himself trying to blow up enemy positions at night and sleeping in ditches by day. Cold, hunger, and danger filled his days, but his dream persisted. On his first furlough, T. S. made his way to Central University and took the entrance examination. He wanted to be ready to go to college as soon as the war was over. Astonished at the boy's high marks, the administrator called T. S. to his office.

"We have decided," said that dignified gentleman, "that you should stay in the university to finish your education. China will need all her brilliant young men to lead her when the fighting is done. We have arranged to extend your furlough from the army."

But life at the university was far from studious and peaceful. The bombing raids increased—so much so that the students were soon spending more time in the shelters than in the classroom. The authorities decided to move the whole university to the westernmost part of China. Day after day, students and faculty tramped through cold, rain, and mud, occasionally pausing by the side of a road to hold a hurried class session between bombings.

Every day T. S. saw hordes of refugees, starving children, and farmers with no work—their fields burned, their crops plundered. At last he could stand it no longer. He knew he must help his country right then in some way or other. He left the university and returned to the army. It was during these days, as he sat tapping out messages in code, that his dream seemed to grow dim. He had given up his chance at the university, and wondered whether he would ever be able to continue his studies.

As day succeeded day, T. S. grew more and more disheartened. His country was in trouble, his own plans had been postponed, possibly never to come true, and he was far from home. Actually, he was more discouraged about China than about himself. The war had ended and there was much talk of communism, of equality and of prosperity for everybody. But T. S. was not convinced. Somehow he could not see that things were improving for the people he knew.

Then one day he met some Christian missionaries. They seemed to like him, even though he was not a Christian. They even invited him to visit them in their homes. Soon T. S. found that he could talk to these people about his country, for they, too, were worried about China's new government.

"I thought everything would be normal when the war was over," he said to them, "but how much does the new government care about the people? The officials live in ease and wealth while our people die in the streets from hunger. The Communists tell us that China's problems can all be solved by their help, that they have the answer to our poverty and need. Hundreds of students are joining their party."

"Believe me, T. S.," one missionary answered, "theirs is not the answer. We Christians have come to help the Chinese people learn to live as brothers. We believe as Jesus taught, that we must 'love one another, for love is of God.'"

To a boy reared in a strict Buddhist home, this was a new idea. It was in his mind constantly as he saw his new Christian friends spending their days helping all the Chinese who needed help. Their lives, as well as their teaching, persuaded Ton-Shun Chang to become a Christian.

As Communists gained more and more power in his country, life became dangerous for T. S. because he had worked for the United States Information Service in China. His friends persuaded him to apply for a scholarship to the United States. He won it and enrolled in the School of Journalism of Syracuse University in New York. His dream was working out! He was sure that soon he would be back in China, building bridges of understanding, now needed more than ever, through newspapers.

At Syracuse, T. S. soon became "Tom" to everyone on the campus. He made many friends. Almost any day he could be seen on the steps of the library, the center of a group of laughing students. Whenever a joke was told, Tom would double up with laughter, slap his knees, and laugh, "Oh my, oh my!" He looked so comical as he did this that it was hard to tell whether the students were laughing at the joke, or at Tom's enjoyment of it.

When the day came that Tom received his Master's degree

he felt that his dream was nearly fulfilled. Now he was ready to go back to China.

But the last part of his dream was elusive. Tom found that he could not return to China while the Communists were in power. Suddenly he found himself alone on a rapidly vacating campus. His friends had all accepted positions on various newspapers. Only Tom was left, without a job, without money, without a home. He was close to panic, but no one would have guessed. His laugh was as merry and his handclasp as warm and friendly as ever as he wished his friends well. Finally, the editor of a small town newspaper came to the campus, desperately looking for a reporter. He was not at all sure that Tom would be able to handle the English language, but there was no one else, and so Tom was hired. It was a day of answered prayer.

Tom worked on many newspapers, all over the United States, and in every community he was an active worker in his church. He taught in Sunday schools and made speeches at many meetings. "Christ's Answer to communism" was one of his favorite topics.

Tom's warmth and friendliness won him special notice. One day, an editor called Tom to his office and said that he had been chosen to write a special series of articles. The editor said, "There is a story in every family, if we could get them to tell it. And they'll tell it to you, because they will feel you're really interested."

And so began a series of more than three hundred articles,

entitled "Meet Tom Chang." Each article carried his picture and signature. In the newspaper world, Tom Chang had reached the top.

One day, at a weekend church conference, Tom was sitting around a campfire with a class of high school students. He had been talking to them about the service God wanted from them. Then soberly he said, "Maybe your plans and dreams won't work out. Mine haven't. I wanted to publish newspapers in China, to build bridges of understanding with the rest of the world. But here I am in the United States, and not helping my people at all."

Then as the flames from the fire flared up, Tom's mood suddenly changed. "Oh my, oh my!" he exclaimed. He slapped his knee as he spoke. The young people looked up in surprise.

"Bridges have two ends! How blind can I be? God simply wants me to begin here and build from West to East, instead of the way I had planned it!"

QUESTIONS

1. How can newspapers help to build bridges of understanding? Can you think of other ways to help bring understanding between peoples?

2. How can a newspaperman be a Christian missionary in his daily work?

4 *They Changed a Village*

PAUL and SUZANNE LANDIS

Sanna Landis smiled and shook her head as she watched her husband drive the sputtering Model A Ford back and forth in the school yard of Sandy Lake. A dozen youngsters, packed into the old auto, screamed with excitement at each turn. After driving the car back and forth several times, Paul opened the doors and shooed the children home. "Ride's all over for today," he called. "Come back tomorrow!"

Paul smiled as he walked over to where his wife was standing, remembering her words about the car. "Why in the world did you buy that?" she had asked. "There's no place you can go with it. It's a waste of $125.00, if you ask me! At least with the Cessna 180 we can get from here to Calling Lake if the water is clear enough for the pontoons, or frozen enough for it to land on skis."

"Why, Sanna!" Paul had answered. "No $125.00 on earth ever bought more fun than the kids will have riding back and forth across the school yard in that old car! When they get tired of riding to the fence and back, we'll let them work on its insides. That'll be good training for them for the future."

Now, he heard Sanna saying, "Honestly, Paul. You're a bigger youngster than all the rest!" She smiled at her tall young husband. She had been so eager to come up to Northern Alberta with him, but if she had known what it would really be like, would she still have come? She honestly did not know. The director of the Mennonite Voluntary Services had spoken very frankly about the needs of the community, but somehow it all sounded different when they were sitting back there in his office.

She would never forget the sight of these few log cabins when their pilot had announced "Sandy Lake, folks!" Or how, when they had pushed open their cabin door, the mud had dropped through the chinks in the roof onto the brown wrapping paper ceiling. Yes—*wrapping paper*.

"Welcome to your new home," Ike, the unit leader, had said. And she had thought, welcome indeed!

One dim electric light bulb was hanging over the small wood stove. On seeing it, Sanna had suddenly remembered what her friend over in Calling Lake had said: "There may not be any roads into Sandy Lake, but you have electricity there, which we don't have here!" Electricity! One bulb!

Now that they were settled into their new life, Paul and Sanna found that there were some fixed parts of every day that could not be changed. First there was water to be fetched from the lake.

"And don't forget," Ike had reminded them on one of his trips into Sandy Lake, "later in the season you can't drink lake water. It gets thicker than pea soup."

"What do we do then?" Paul had asked.

"You take the boat up the lake till you come to a small river. Water's pretty good there. But I'll have to admit, wash-day is pretty discouraging!"

Then there was the everyday problem of wood. The black stove in the house had seemed small when they first saw it, but it ate up huge quantities of wood, all of which had to be sawed and split. Each evening Paul sawed the logs into one-foot lengths, split them with an axe, then lugged them into the house for the always hungry stove.

Their only contact with the outside world, except for Ike's irregular visits, was the radio. Paul was a part of the Canadian National Telegraph chain, and thus had to report on the air twice a day, if possible—once at nine o'clock in the morning and again at one in the afternoon.

This had often been annoying to Sanna until the day in early summer, when Jeanne got hurt. Sanna, busy with her ironing, heard a feeble cry from the yard. Before she could put down her iron and go to the door, the young neighbor girl stumbled across the yard, holding her right arm tightly against her side. She almost fell against the door as Sanna opened it.

"Why, Jeanne! Whatever is wrong? Is it your arm? How did you hurt it?" As she talked, Sanna tried to make the girl comfortable. Then she called Paul.

"My horse, Pepper, threw me," explained Jeanne. "Something must have frightened him. Oooh!" she moaned, as Paul tried to look at the injured arm.

"Now, young lady," he said calmly, "you just sit here and let Sanna wait on you. I'll call for help." And with that he was at the radio, calling for the plane.

"My folks are out fishing," Jeanne said weakly.

"Yes, I know," soothed Sanna, "but don't worry. We'll let them know what happened. The plane will soon be here, and you'll be on your way to Athabasca to have your shoulder fixed. These pills will stop the pain a bit."

It was some kind of record they set that day. Forty minutes from the time Paul called until the plane arrived from Calling Lake. Five minutes to put Jeanne on the plane and send her off to the hospital at Athabasca, approximately one hundred air miles away.

"Oh, Paul!" said the relieved Sanna. "What would we have

done without that radio? But what if her arm wasn't even broken? Oh, I hope we did the right thing!"

It was broken and badly dislocated. Jeanne had her arm and shoulder in a cast all summer.

Other days, however, were not so serious. In fact, life often seemed dull to Sanna. Here in the Northern woods, far away from all the problems of a troubled world, she often felt useless and unneeded.

Yes, she often wondered whether she would have come, if she had really known what Sandy Lake was like. . . .

"Why so serious, Sanna?" Paul's voice jolted her back to the present.

"Oh, just thinking about the report to be filled out tonight."

Later, after supper and the dishes, Sanna sat under the small light bulb, scratching her curls with the tip of her pencil. "It's really hard to describe my part of our community service for new volunteers. I've been reading through our reports, but it all seems so unimportant, somehow."

Paul smiled at his troubled wife. "Read what you've written," he suggested.

She chewed the end of her pencil, then read from her list:

Gave haircuts to four boys.

"Adopted" 4-year-old Elsie Gambler for a night when "Old Sophie" was dying.

Worked with three girls to make ninety bottles of root beer for the picnic.

Took buckets of tomato plants and marigolds, grown from seed, over to the Bigstones and helped them plant them in their garden.

Worked with the youth fellowship to fry one hundred doughnuts for a Halloween party.

Did the washing for the Beavers while the mother was in the hospital at Edmonton for six weeks.

Sanna laid the paper down on the table. "It doesn't seem like much to encourage new volunteers—or old ones, either!" There was a suspicious catch in her voice.

Paul rubbed his forehead. "You forgot a few things," he said slowly. "You substituted for me at school while I went moose hunting. You taught first and second grade all year. You plan Youth Nite every Thursday night, the Christmas concert and all the other parties. You canned enough food for us for the next year, and cooked with some of the girls. And you taught them to sew." He put his hand on her shoulder encouragingly, then went back to correcting papers.

Suddenly Sanna interrupted him. "Paul! I never saw this before!" She held up a sheet of paper and read:

ZERO DAY

Problems: Discouragement.

Lost my temper with the kids.

Worried about uncompleted work.

Needed: More love, joy, peace, patience, and a determination to do the right.

Paul reached for the paper. "Oh, I meant to tear that up. It was just a bad day. I didn't mean it!"

"Paul, you never told me you felt this way."

"I tell you, I don't! I was ashamed as soon as I wrote it, and I wrote another report that month."

"Well, that settles it," said Sanna stubbornly. "When we go on our vacation this summer, we're going to stay. We won't come back here!"

"Now, Sanna, listen," began Paul.

"No, you listen!" interrupted Sanna. "We'll have finished the two years we signed up for. So there's no reason why we can't go ahead and look for a place where you can teach in a high school, as you are trained to do. I haven't felt that I was accomplishing anything here, but I was willing to stick it out because I thought you liked it."

"But, Sanna, it is a challenge to me to teach so many children of so many different ages, scattered through eight grades. I really like it. You know that."

"Well, maybe you do, but I don't! Let's go home."

Paul merely grunted and went on grading his papers. No use arguing with a woman whose mind is made up!

But vacation was a long way off, and their days were filled with the usual tasks. Paul and Sanna did not discuss their decision to leave—not even between themselves. Sanna kept putting off packing and the other things that would have to be done before they could leave. After all, there was plenty of time.

Early spring brought a pleasant surprise to the Landises, especially to Sanna. All of Sandy Lake was invited to a party. Usually the villagers were far too busy with fishing, trapping, net mending, and garden work to have time for get-togethers. But the Yellow Knees, the Indian leaders of Sandy Lake, were going to have a party.

When Sanna and Paul arrived at the Yellow Knees', Sanna noticed several things that were new and different. The cabin was very clean. The windows were hung with gay kitchen towels made into curtains, much like the ones she had used to brighten her own kitchen.

The families were all dressed with care. Many of the children had new dresses and new moccasins. Mrs. Yellow Knee's meal was well cooked. There was moose steak, with mashed potatoes, tomato salad, and homemade ice cream.

After dinner, Mrs. Yellow Knee stood up at Sanna's side. Using Cree expressions in her English, she said shyly, "My girls visit you in your house. It is the same as ours, but always shining and clean. They help me to sew curtains like yours. They tell me, 'We should eat salad every day.' We scrub floor many times to make it shine like yours. When you first came, you were very different from us. We felt strange with you. We see you hauling in wood; we see you carry water for your wash, same as we do. You live like us, we live more like you. Now we are friends; we do not feel strange with you. You help us with our work, you take care of our young people. We need you."

As she spoke, the bright eyes of the other women lighted in agreement, and the youngsters were smiling. Sanna felt a tightness in her throat.

When Ike came in the plane that week, he knocked on the door of the Landis cabin.

"Folks, it's time for me to make arrangements for your replacements. Now just when, exactly, are you planning to leave?"

Before Paul could pick up a calendar, Sanna answered, "We aren't leaving . . . at least we're coming back after our vacation. This is our home." Then, meekly, she turned to her husband. "Isn't it, Paul?"

Paul was too surprised to answer. No use arguing with a woman whose mind is made up. It was easier simply to nod and smile.

QUESTIONS

1. Think about the contributions to the community that the Landises made. What kind of service might you do in your community?

2. If you had not been told that Paul and Sanna were Mennonites, would you have known they were Christians? How could you tell?

5 *From Despair to Hope*

DOCTOR MARY VERGHESE

"Joseph . . . is it Joseph . . .?" The artist was uncertain. He peered up from his drawing on the sidewalk in Vellore, India, at a well-dressed young man.

"Yes, I am Joseph," said the smiling young man. "What marvelous drawings you have made! May I help you?"

Clutching a piece of charcoal in his clawlike hands, Muthu, the artist, looked at him again in puzzled wonderment. "I think I know you," he said slowly. "You look like Joseph from my hometown in Andhra, but . . ." his voice trailed off in hesitation.

Joseph squatted down beside him. "Yes, I come from Andhra. You are wondering about my hands. Several years ago they were as crippled with leprosy as yours." Gently he touched the artist's hands. "But they were rebuilt right here in Vellore at a Christian hospital. Yours can be as straight as mine."

Unable to comprehend such a miracle, the artist gazed at Joseph in silence.

"What are you doing here with your drawings?" Joseph asked.

The artist hung his head. "I am begging for a few coins," he said. "When it was known that I had leprosy, my family threw me out. I go from place to place. With my charcoal I sketch on the sidewalk and hope for a few coins to be tossed my way. But my hands are getting more and more crippled. Soon I shall not be able to hold the charcoal." His tone was one of deep despair.

Joseph could understand, for he had known that hopelessness, too. "Let me help you up," he said kindly. "I'd like to show you what is being done here in Vellore for people like us."

Joseph led his friend a few blocks down the street toward a modern building. "That is the Christian Medical College Hospital, where I now work. I type up records, interview patients, and talk to people who should come here," he said.

The two men walked around the hospital and into the beautiful new Physical Medicine and Rehabilitation Building. "We are very proud of this building," Joseph went on. "Thousands of people have been helped here. Here, let's walk down this ramp to the basement. I want you to see some of the patients.

"In this room," Joseph said, opening a door, "people are soaking their hands in wax and massaging their fingers with oil. This makes their skin soft and pliable before surgery. Some of them are using splints, too, to make their fingers as straight as possible before their operations."

Muthu noticed with amazement how cheerful all the patients looked and how warmly they greeted Joseph. "What happens on the other floors?" he asked, as he and Joseph started back up the ramp.

"The second floor is given over to patients who are recovering from surgery. On the ground floor is the gymnasium, which is where I'm taking you now."

Having arrived at the gymnasium, the young artist gazed in astonishment as people on crutches slowly pulled themselves up stairs built with handrails. He saw patients slowly putting one braced leg before another, as they held on to the bars. Others were pulling weights up a pulley.

"What are they doing?" Muthu asked in a whisper.

"Ask them," Joseph smiled.

But the girl who was working at the nearest pulley heard the question and smiled at the two young men. "I am working to get back the muscles in my arm," she explained. "I have two little children and want to be able to hold them. A mother who cannot pick up her children is only half a mother."

Joseph noticed that the artist was showing signs of weariness. "Sit down here a minute," he said, pointing to a nearby bench. "It would take all day for you to see all the work that goes on here. We have people who make special splints and braces for the leprosy patients. Some have to have special shoes. Some need plastic braces for their backs. All these are made here so that they can be fitted to the patient. And, four miles away, up on the college hill, is the New Life Center. There young men who have been leprosy patients are trained in weaving, carpentry, and toymaking, so that they can support themselves."

The artist held his clawlike hand to his head. "I can't believe all this. Who knows so well how to help us in all these ways?"

"I was going to tell you about Dr. Verghese," Joseph said. "But first I wanted you to see something of the work here in the Physical Medicine Building."

"Why haven't I heard of it before?" the artist asked in wonder.

"It's all very new," Joseph explained. "We have two Indian men, two Canadian women, and one American man. They are our physiotherapists. That is the name for people who help us to exercise our bodies in the pool and in the gymnasium so that we can retrain our muscles to do their work. Better even than their own work is their training of future therapists. Six of their students will graduate this summer. They too will train others. That is how Christian Medical College works."

The artist paused, seemingly silenced by all the new ideas that had come to him. Joseph felt that they had walked enough for one day.

"Come over to my room and we'll cool off with a glass of lime juice. Then I'll tell you about Dr. Mary Verghese, who is the head of our Physical Medicine Department."

In his room, Joseph had Muthu lie down on his cot to rest. He placed the cool lime juice so that the deformed hands could hold the plastic cup. Before he began to tell his story, he held out his hands for Muthu to inspect. "See? It is almost impossible to see the scars on my hands where new muscles have been grafted. That's because of the skill of Dr. Verghese."

Muthu looked at the remade hands and then stretched his own deformed claw-like hands alongside of them. "Is your Dr. Verghese a miracle worker?"

Joseph smiled. "With God's help—yes. Dr. Mary came to this hospital to train as a doctor, and it soon became evident that she had great skill as a surgeon. Dr. Ida Scudder, who was head of Vellore Christian Medical College at that time, wanted her to work with women and children. Dr. Mary planned to get some further training in Bombay." Joseph paused and his eyes had a sober, faraway look.

Muthu sat up and looked at Joseph. "But something happened—is it not so?"

Joseph rose to pour more lime juice for his friend. Then he

turned and looked out of the window for a long minute. "I was not here at the time, but I have heard the story from some of the people who took part in it." He drew a deep breath and looked his new friend full in the face.

"One day, the interns who had finished their term of work were going on a picnic. Dr. Mary Verghese was asked to go with them. They rode in a station wagon driven by one of our regular hospital chauffeurs. But among the group was a young student who had just received his driving license and wanted to drive. For a long time he drove well. Then the station wagon came up to a slow-moving bus. Each time the young driver tried to pass the bus, the bus driver pulled out and refused to allow him to pass. This made the young driver so angry that he completely lost his temper and forced a passing. He swerved to miss a bridge, the station wagon turned over and rolled down a steep embankment. Everyone was seriously hurt but Dr. Mary was so terribly injured they thought she was dead. All were brought back to the hospital.

"For weeks, they despaired of Dr. Mary's life. Then, as she slowly regained consciousness, they found that her spine had been injured and that she would never walk again."

A shocked silence fell over the young Indian artist as Joseph told the story. An unbelieving look came over his face as he said, "But she did recover! Didn't you tell me that she was the head of the Physical Medicine Department here and that she had operated on your hands?"

"Yes," Joseph asserted. "But she cannot walk."

"A doctor who cannot walk?" Muthu exclaimed. "How can she do her work then?"

"At first she could do nothing for herself. But through years of agony and pain she trained herself to operate her own wheelchair, to dress herself, to move herself from her chair to her bed, to feed herself—even to perform surgery! She was the one who restored my hands to their usefulness."

Muthu shook his head in complete amazement. "I cannot comprehend this," he said. "Why does she want to do this? Has she no family who could care for her?"

"Her brother is a doctor. She has a large and loving family who would gladly care for her for the rest of her life. But Dr. Mary has said many times that she knows God saved her life for some purpose and she wants to serve him as best she can. She became interested in rehabilitation of patients when she herself was able to regain so much independence."

"I still don't see how a woman could suffer like this and still want to help others." Muthu held his glass in his misshapen hands. "I hate myself and the world," he said bitterly. "I hate my family for turning me out. I even hate the people who throw me the coins out of pity and who never see that my drawings are good. They are good enough to merit more than a few coins."

"Someday soon you will meet Dr. Verghese," Joseph said earnestly. "Tomorrow, I will make a report on you. Perhaps we can set the wheels turning and you will soon be earning your way again. I hope that she will feel that something can be done for your hands. Such talent as yours is sorely needed in this world. Sleep here tonight."

"It's . . . I only wish to earn a living," Muthu spoke hesitatingly. "I feel less than a man when I cannot use my hands. I stumble as I try to walk. I want to feel human again."

Joseph understood only too well. "Our biggest problem, we leprosy patients," he said, deliberately reminding Muthu that they were alike, "is to get back our dignity, to be someone again. That is what Dr. Verghese has given us above all else. Her life of service and her inner beauty make us realize what a life rebuilt in Christ can be."

"There I do not follow you, Joseph. My people are Hindu. I know nothing of what you say," said Muthu.

Joseph was about to explain further about his newfound faith when he was interrupted. A low sweet voice was calling, "Joseph, Joseph, can you help me?"

Quickly the two men went out into the corridor. There Muthu saw a lady with the kindest face he had ever seen. Dark eyebrows shadowed merry eyes. Smooth shining hair, drawn back in a knot, framed a face bearing a look of infinite joy and pain.

"Joseph," Dr. Mary's voice reached him as she spoke to his friend. "Look what I have done. My sari blew in the breeze from the window and it is caught in the wheels of my chair. Please could you help me?"

Joseph bent quickly to release the sari, and introduced Muthu to the doctor, describing his friend's great talent in art.

Dr. Mary looked up at the boy. She took his hand in hers and looked at it with professional skill. "I see no reason, Muthu, why your hands cannot be straightened and made useful again, if you have the courage to endure the discipline and the patience to retrain them. It takes a great deal of both, don't you agree, Joseph?"

The three paused in the corridor of the Vellore hospital, united in their knowledge of uselessness and rejection. But Muthu felt that the doctor and Joseph shared a beautiful secret—a deeper fellowship in their knowledge of hope instead of despair. Now his hands were being lifted again in the cool hands of the doctor.

"A famous poet said:

My hand alone my work can do.[1]

Your hands will do your work again, Muthu. Come to clinic tomorrow, and we will arrange an operation." With a wave she was gone.

Muthu stood transfixed. "Dr. Mary Verghese," he repeated, wonderingly.

QUESTIONS

1. Read about leprosy in the encyclopedia. Why are people so much more afraid of leprosy than of other contagious diseases?

2. Muthu was a Hindu. Joseph tried to explain that it was because Dr. Mary was a Christian that she had been able to find courage to start again after her accident. How would you explain this to Muthu?

[1] Izaak Walton, The Compleat Angler. "The Angler's Song."

6 *Torchbearer of Scholarship*

HAMILTON HOLMES

Hamp was smiling to himself as he stood on the steps in front of Turner High. The warmth of Atlanta's spring sunshine felt wonderful; it was good to be alive!

Senior year had been the best year yet, he reflected. President of his class, elected to the All-State Football Team, hero of football and basketball games, Hamilton Holmes had filled his days with fun and friends. And now he had just received the biggest honor of all.

A cheerful voice interrupted his thoughts. "Congratulations, Hamp! I knew you would make valedictorian." Hamp grinned as Charlayne came through the glass door with a swish of her skirt.

"Hi! I've been waiting for you," he said. They started down the steps. "Still planning on going to Wayne State this fall?"

"I think so, Hamp. They offer a good journalism course, which is what I am looking for."

"How about changing your mind and coming with me to the University of Georgia in Athens?"

Charlayne gasped as she turned her dark eyes to his. Then she shook her head in pretended sympathy. "Poor Hamp! I declare the sun's surely got too strong for you. Here, come and sit in the shade and rest." And laughingly she pulled him over to the shady crepe myrtle.

"Hamp, have you forgotten our governor?" Rolling her eyes, Charlayne struck an orator's pose, as she imitated the governor vowing to keep Negroes out of the university. She rolled her eyes, thumped a tree with her fist, and spoke in thundering tones.

Hamp's face lit up with his slow easy grin, and his voice had just a hint of a chuckle. "Char, you and I might make him eat those words. How about it? Are you game?"

The University of Georgia! It seemed like a crazy dream. Hamp had always known that he would go to college. His father, mother, and grandfather were all college graduates.

Hamp had always planned to get his pre-med college training at Morehouse in Atlanta, as his grandfather had done. But as senior year came to a close, Hamp and Charlayne talked more and more about going to the University of Georgia.

"What do you think about my going to the university, Gramp?" Hamp asked, as he swung himself up onto the doctor's desk.

"Get off my desk, Hamp. I declare you act like you did when you were seven, and now you're seventeen!" Grandfather sat in his consulting room, looking over his glasses at his favorite grandson. "I'd say that depends upon you, entirely, Hamp. Medicine gets more complicated every day, and the best preparation you can get is none too good. But," he looked thoughtfully at the boy who had climbed down from the desk and was slouching in the patient's chair, "have you the courage, Hamp? Can you stick it out when they try to keep you out? Will you be able to take it if you do get in, and the other students show you that they don't want a Negro there with them?"

"Why, Gramp, I've always been able to make friends. I figure I could get on the basketball or football team. They've got a great football team, and I sure would like to try out for it. I'd get to know at least a few people that way."

The Holmes' lawyer who talked to Charlayne and Hamp said the same things Gramp had said—over and over.

Back and forth the lawyer bent and twisted the paper clip in his hand. "It all depends upon how much disappointment you can take, you two, and still keep your heads. It will take a court case and a miracle to get you in—but if we do, can you take it and stay there?"

Hamp was growing more and more convinced that this was something he had to do. Everyone seemed to doubt his courage, or his ability, or something.

"Mr. Hollowell," he said, with a glance at Charlayne to make sure she was with him, "you get us into the university. Once we're in, we'll stick it out. Won't we, Char?"

"If you will, I will, Hamp. How about it, Mr. Hollowell?"

So the applications were filled in. Mr. Hollowell showed them to the other lawyers who were working with him. Hamp's record from Turner High showed a total of thirty-six A's and six B's. He had won all the athletic honors possible. Valedictorian of his class. Charlayne, third in her class, showed up as an excellent student with a special talent for writing. Mr. Hollowell looked at his law partner and then at the two eager students. "They can't refuse records like these," he said.

The weeks went by. The university was called to court to state why they were not accepting the two Negro students. Hamp sat with his hands clenched and heard the admissions officer say, "Your Honor, we don't feel that the boy is qualified." Only Gramp sitting beside him heard Hamp say, "I'll show them." And Gramp sighed as he said, "That's my boy."

August passed and September came. Still the university gave no answer. Hamp had to get started at college. The medical course he had planned for himself was long; he had no years to waste. By the end of September, Charlayne had flown to Detroit to enter Wayne State University and Hamp was enrolled in Morehouse College in Atlanta.

In spite of the disappointment of not going to Athens, Hamp loved Morehouse. He was as popular there as he had been at Turner High. He made friends easily. He kept up his outstanding scholastic record and found time to star on the basketball team, too.

Almost before he knew it, a year and a half had passed. Hamp was a happy and successful student at the top of his class, a top athlete, well-liked by his classmates and surrounded by his family.

The court case dragged on. Hamp almost forgot that he had applied for entrance to the university. But he had a sudden reminder. He was poring over his books one cold night when the telephone rang.

"Pack your bags, Hamp. We're off!" It was Don Hollowell's voice, excitement barely concealed.

"Where are we going, Don?" Hamp had hardly come out of his thoughts on the science paper lying before him.

"To Athens, Hamp. I've just called Charlayne. She's flying down tomorrow. The judge ordered the University of Georgia to admit you Monday morning."

"Don, I don't want to go. Things are going well here at Morehouse. I think the university would just be a headache. It was a wild scheme anyway."

"I'm sorry, Hamp." Don's voice was the firm one now. "The chances of thousands of Negro students are riding on your graduating from the University of Georgia. You can't let them down now."

Hamp knew it was the truth. If he could graduate from the University of Georgia, he would open the doors to others of his race. Hamilton Holmes, an "A" student, a top athlete, had it in his hands to open that door to others.

But Morehouse was such fun. Why not finish out the year there and then go to the university his last two years? He put the question to Don Hollowell.

"Sorry, Hamp. Too much depends upon you."

Monday morning was cold and damp. Charlayne and Hamp walked across the University of Georgia campus to the Admissions Office. No one seemed to notice them. Most of the students had not yet returned from their two-day break after exams. The campus was quiet and lonesome. Hamp shivered under his jacket. The newspaper reporters surrounded them, pushing their microphones at their faces.

"What are your plans?" they asked over and over.

Hamp, chilled by the wind blowing across the campus and dismayed at the cold unfriendliness he had encountered, spoke more gruffly than he had intended. "To graduate," was the only reply the reporters could get from him.

The day was busy. Cards and forms to be filled in. Books to be bought. Charlayne's luggage to take to her room in the dormitory. Hamp's room to be rented off campus. Permits needed to park their cars on campus. Schedule cards to be made out and handed in.

Two days passed like a dream. Everything was quiet and very orderly. But on the third day they found out what life at the university was going to be like. Late in the afternoon on Wednesday, a group of noisy students gathered outside Charlayne's window in the dorm. They carried a large bed sheet on which they had printed, "CHAR, GO HOME!" As more and more people collected, the temper of the crowd seemed to rise. They shouted angrily. They grew wild and uncontrolled.

Suddenly there was a sound of breaking glass. Someone had thrown a coke bottle through Charlayne's window. Then there was crash after crash as the students, completely out of control, threw stone after stone through the shattered window into Charlayne's room.

The students had forgotten their dean. With no regard for his own safety, Dr. Tate walked into the crowd. He called student after student by name, taking from them their identity cards without which they could not get into the dining rooms. Coldly, he ordered them back to their rooms. Then, late as it was, he drove Charlayne and Hamp back to Atlanta so that they would be safe.

This seemed a good opportunity for the university to refuse Char and Hamp all over again. Again the judge stepped in with an order stating that they must be allowed in. This time neither of them hesitated. Wednesday had given them some taste of the job that lay before them. They were ready now to accept the challenge.

Dr. Tate met them, and as he talked to Don Hollowell and the two students, Hamp glimpsed for the first time how different Athens would be from Morehouse. "As long as your students do not provoke any trouble, Mr. Hollowell, I think we can guarantee their safety." Hamp looked up at the quiet man, who had been so fearless in the face of the mob.

"What does that mean, provoke trouble?" he asked.

Don Hollowell felt he must break the new rules of this new campus to Hamp, who had known nothing but friendliness all his life. "It means never to speak to a white student first, Hamp," he said sadly. "They must always be the ones to start a conversation."

Hamp's dream of making friends on the football team, on the basketball court, suddenly ended. "I suppose there will be no objection to my studying, sir?" he asked the dean.

"Not as long as you do it in your own room," Dr. Tate answered, gravely.

Hamp's fists clenched again as they had done in the court room. "I'll show them!" he said again.

So the days came and went. Hamp kept to his own room and his classroom. He never went near the coke bar. He never studied in the library. Only his eyes strayed longingly to the gym and the stadium. His feet never carried him one step toward them.

He had one goal, one only: to make the best possible

grades. He spent day after day alone, trying to ignore the hurt in his heart, the ache in his throat. He lived for the weekends when he could drive back home, to his family and friends, to someone who would talk to him!

"Isn't there something I can do about this?" He was in Gramp's office, opening his heart to his oldest friend.

"Yes, Hamp, there is." Gramp's voice was calm, but there was love and pity in his eyes. "You can have faith. You've always believed that the Lord would look after you. Now's the time to prove it."

"Surely they can see that I can keep up with the work, Gramp. They can't say I'm not qualified." Hamp sounded a little desperate.

"You can show them something else, Hamp. You can show them that you may be hated, but you don't hate. Someday, these same students will come to know what they missed not knowing you as a friend."

Hamp shrugged his shoulders wearily and said, "I don't know, Gramp. I hope you're right."

At last it was June, 1963. Hamilton Holmes stood among the small group who were graduating with honors. He had received membership in two honor societies. He had been given a scholarship to Emory Medical School. He moved the tassel on his mortarboard from one side to the other, the outward sign that he had graduated. His eye caught the movement of Charlayne's slim hand as she, too, moved her tassel.

He tried to catch her glance, to see if the same thoughts

were passing through her mind as through his. Yes, they had graduated. But from what? From two and a half years of loneliness, of all work and no fun, of homesickness so desperate that it throbbed in his throat and stung his eyes. Two and a half years. For what?

Under his gown, his fingers held a clipping from the university newspaper. The hate-filled words were written on his brain: "Hamilton Holmes entered this university forcibly as an alien. He attended as an alien, and when he graduates, he will graduate as an alien. . . . He could have expected no more. He has received no less. . . ." Slowly his fingers twisted the paper and dropped it on the campus green. But Gramp's words drowned out the spiteful print. "I am hated but I do not hate. Someday, someday . . ."

Graduation was scarcely over when the university officials began processing applications for the summer session. The papers were sorted. The best were passed around for committee approval. One girl's qualifications were unusually good. "Stamp that one 'Approved.'" It was Dean Tate's voice speaking.

The director stamped it and then glanced at it again. "This girl is a Negro, sir!"

"What of it?" Dean Tate's voice was unruffled. "She's qualified, isn't she?"

Hamilton Holmes, graduate of the University of Georgia, *cum laude*, Phi Beta Kappa, and Phi Kappa Phi, had helped to open the door.

QUESTIONS

1. During his stay at the University of Georgia, Hamilton Holmes found that he was made welcome at the campus fellowship meetings of his church. But the students who were friendly to him at the meetings often passed him by on campus without speaking. Why do you think they did this?

2. Hamilton hoped that having opened the door to Negro students at the University of Georgia, it would be easier for others to attend. Not many have gone to this university yet. Why do you think so few Negroes have followed Hamp and Char?

7 *Painter with Sunlight*

YVONNE WILLIAMS

The blond girl stood at the dormitory window in complete silence. Outside, the first snowflakes were lazily slipping through the air, slowly making a film of white on the lawn outside the window.

Sue, her Canadian roommate, watched Yvonne for a minute, then said a little crossly, "What gives with you? You look completely rapt. Anyone would think you had never seen snow before!"

Yvonne Williams turned with a half apologetic smile. "I'm sorry, did you say something? I'm afraid I didn't hear."

"Oh, never mind," Sue said, a little ungraciously. "I wanted to remind you that we have to unpack our suitcases and put away our things before we go down to dinner. OK with you if I use the drawers on the left? They're handier to my bed."

"That's perfectly all right, Suzanne." Yvonne spoke with an odd accent that Sue couldn't identify and her eyes had strayed again to the thickening snow outside. "I never realized that it came in such tiny, beautiful pieces," she said half to herself.

"I don't get you at all. You act as though you've never seen snow before. Here, catch this, will you, and stick it in the corner there behind the door?" And Sue threw one ski boot to her new roommate. "You'll find out I'm not very neat."

Once or twice more, Yvonne stopped unpacking to look out of the dormer window. She couldn't seem to tear her eyes away from the snowflakes now coming down faster and faster. Once or twice she started to tell Suzanne that she had guessed correctly. She, Yvonne, had never seen snow before. In her home in Trinidad, far away in the West Indies, she saw the sun-sparkles on the blue wavelets on the shore near her home, but snow, never!

But Yvonne's throat was dry with shyness. She envied the ease with which Sue kept up a running fire of talk as she tossed things right and left into drawers that Yvonne knew were getting too stuffed to close.

"You've just come, I hear," Sue said. "Well, you'll like it. Really, it's a dilly of a school. Of course some of the mistresses are awfully heavy-handed when it comes to homework. They act as if there was nothing else to be done but algebra or French irregular verbs. Oh, good, here's my other ski boot. I wouldn't do very well on the slopes with only one boot."

"Ski?" Yvonne finally got out the word, pronouncing it "shee." "Do we take ski lessons at school here? How odd! I hadn't thought about it."

"You better think. And you better learn to say s-k-i like 'skee.' Are you English or something?"

"Yes." Yvonne's face was rosy pink and Sue's laugh took away the courage she was trying to muster up to tell Suzanne about her long trip to Toronto.

"Where on earth do you come from?" she asked.

Catching Yvonne's half-whispered answer, Sue said brusquely, "Trinidad? Where's that?" and hurried out of the room.

It seemed an eternity before dinner was over, the talk to new students by the headmistress finished, and the girls dismissed for the night.

Almost every girl in the dorm had to traipse in to visit Sue. "She must be the most popular girl in school," Yvonne thought miserably. "She'll hate being stuck in a room with me. I wish I could talk as gaily as they do."

In the dark, Yvonne lay in a tight knot in her bed. Sue had thrown herself gracefully across the bed, pulled up the wool coverlet, called "Goodnight" sleepily, and in a minute or two, her regular breathing told Yvonne she was sound asleep. Feeling lonely, Yvonne tried talking to herself as the girls had tonight. "Oh, you should have seen the plane I took up to Toronto. It was a scream. So antique. It belonged in a show!"

She tried again, "Oh, yes," she drawled as the tall chestnut colored brunette had done. "You should have seen the copilot, girls. He was the dreamiest!" She would never be able to talk to these chatterboxes.

Too bad that she didn't have some clay, or she could model her lovely home in Trinidad. She could show the girls the snow-white gulls. She never tired of watching them swoop down to float on the water. She could make them see the folks going to market with gay bandannas on their heads, or huge woven flower-trimmed hats. Yvonne knew that her fingers talked better than her tongue.

As days and nights passed, Yvonne felt as homesick as ever. Once she tried to tell Sue about the first day in the room. "Father had a lovely painting of a snow scene in his study. But the snow was deep and thick. I had never stopped to think how it got to be that way. I was so surprised to see how little the flakes were," she said.

"So that's it," Sue murmured, and out the door she went.

"I'll write and tell Mother that I can't stand it here. I want to go home," Yvonne said, fiercely, as she looked at the door Sue had closed firmly. "I'll write now, before class!"

But when she sat at the window with her writing pad on her knee, she remembered the plans her family had made so that she might have a good education and later be able to enter any college she wanted. She couldn't just quit like a small child. Instead, she found herself writing:

There are some very interesting times every day and I can't decide which I enjoy most. I love the art classes. You will be glad to see what I have done. The teacher likes my modeling. She is going to help me cast one or two of my things.

I love my ski lessons. I remember now not to say "shee!" I am learning to skate, too. In two weeks we are going to have our winter carnival. The girls have asked me to help them with their snow sculpture.

We have to go to chapel twice a day. Most of the girls think it is a bore. But I hear the stories read from the Bible, and I love to look up and see the stories shining in the beautiful stained glass windows. For those few minutes, I forget that I am so far away from you. You seem to be with me.

The years passed at boarding school. And now they were seniors. Yvonne was never able to join the chattering crowd, but she won their respect by her artistic talent. Indeed, she brought honor after honor to the school by the prizes she won in that field. The girls were quick to call on her for anything that needed an artist's touch.

Chapel was still her favorite time of the day. No one could talk there, and she was one of the group as she sat in silence.

Day after day, she heard about the people who had already become familiar friends to her.

"Zaccheus!" she thought. "What a picture he would make! Peering down through the leaves! I know just how he felt when everyone was talking about him as if he weren't there. The girls do that to me, too!"

For the senior girls, there was only one subject of conversation these days—the colleges or finishing schools they would attend next year. "What are your plans, Yvonne?" someone would ask carelessly and before Yvonne could collect her thoughts, the conversation would have taken a new turn.

"Just as well," Yvonne said to herself. "Suppose I was honest? Suppose I just said, 'Well, as a matter of fact, I don't plan to go to school or college. I'm going home to Trinidad and keep house for my family.' They would think me definitely odd."

But a wonderful scholarship to an art school changed all her "going home" plans. And once more, Yvonne faced the possible torture of a school where everyone talked so easily and where the silent ones were always shut out, designated as "odd."

However, art school was completely different. Here everyone seemed to be an individual; each one had a means of expression. Yvonne's world reached out to new horizons. There was color, form, loveliness everywhere. And she threw herself into her work with a passion that surprised even the most dedicated.

One day, she was introduced to stained glass. In complete absorption she watched the design drawn on the glass, the rich wonderful glass that transformed the magic of sunlight into new beauty for man. And as surely as art school had given her new life, Yvonne now knew that it had given her the work she would do.

A thousand designs came to her and then a thousand more. She found she was designing the friends she had made from the Bible during chapel hours—Zaccheus, the good shepherd, the Israelite who fell among thieves, the woman at the well. They were her friends, all waiting to be made into rich, glorious colored windows that would help earthbound people to reach out to heaven itself.

Once her art school was finished, Yvonne began her life work. She gathered a team of artists around her. There were Gus and Ellen, also designers, who helped plan the windows. There was also George who put the pieces of glass together in the windows. As the four of them sat in the studio and talked about their work, Yvonne was surprised to find that talking was easy—talking about windows, at least! Maybe it made a difference when you and your friends cared about the same things!

Yvonne had no trouble telling George her ideas and getting his suggestions as to how they could be carried out. When the windows were designed, the drawings made and transferred to glass, they were then fired in an electric kiln. When the firing was over, George took the hundreds of pieces that made up the design, joined them with strips of lead, and completed the story window.

It took a long time to get started. People who want stained glass windows hesitate to trust an unknown artist with the work. Yvonne had very few orders. "Why don't you consider portrait painting or commercial art?" friends suggested. "With your talent you could make a fortune in that field!" The world seemed to be full of people with suggestions for her.

To Yvonne it seemed as if she were back in boarding school. All over again, she felt unable to put into words what was in her heart. To be able to take the noblest Christian ideas, to shape them in perfection of form and color, to pour the magic of sunlight through them, this was to bring God's truth nearer to man in a way he could see it. This was to raise man a little nearer to God.

And so Yvonne Williams lived and breathed and worked at her dream. First of all she found it necessary to build a bridge of trust and understanding with the church people who wanted a stained glass window. Then she took their ideas, translated them into picture stories, and drew them on glass with colors that flowed into the glass itself. When the work was finished, the window became a strong and lasting part of a structure, bringing not only beauty but spiritual uplift to those who saw it.

And what did it do for Yvonne? Listen to what she says: "I have worked at something that is of more interest to me than anything else in the world. How fortunate I am!"

And today, from Newfoundland to British Columbia, and from Toronto to Aklavik, thousands of worshipers have been brought a little closer to God by the Yvonne Williams' windows. The shy girl who once stood tongue-tied, trying to express the beauty of a single snowflake, had found her voice.

QUESTIONS

1. Try to bring to class an article about, or an illustration of stained glass windows. Then try to learn through research what steps the artist takes from the original design to the firing, fitting together, and leading of the pieces. In addition to the magic of the designer, what other quality would you think workers with stained glass must have?

2. How is the making and designing of a stained glass window a way of preaching a sermon? Tell how it might help people.

8 Long Fight for Freedom

ALBERT LUTHULI

Albert John Luthuli sat in his office at Adams College, Natal, South Africa. His usually cheerful brown face wore a look of deep concentration as he turned from one to another of his visitors, seated before him. He seemed to be fumbling for words.

"I don't know. . . . I couldn't. . . ."

The oldest of the men interrupted him. "We realize that this is a tremendous sacrifice we are asking of you," he said, "as well as a great favor to us. Since your uncle died, the Umvoti Mission Reserve has not lived in peace and happiness as it did when he was our chief. Since you lived with him as a child, you must remember how much he tried to help us solve our problems with the government, how ready he was to listen to our troubles. Now Groutville is having many problems, and our people do not think that our present chief is doing a good job. They want you to be our chief."

"We believe," said another, "that you are the only one who can help us straighten out our tribal problems."

"Gentlemen," said Luthuli, "I am pleased and touched that you have come to me with this offer. I should like to follow in my Uncle Martin's footsteps. But my life is here at Adams. Here I teach the music I love, and the language of our people. Here I work with eager young people who will, in turn, go out to teach other children of South Africa. Then, too, I think I am too young to be a good chief."

"But you already understand so well the duties of a chief," argued the first visitor. "And we—your people—are asking for you on the mission reserve."

"I must have some time to consider this," replied Luthuli. "I want to talk it over with my wife. Give me time to go home to Groutville. In a few days you shall have your answer."

Courteously he said goodbye to his guests and sat down to think at his desk, the only "office" he had had for fifteen years. To be chief of a mission reserve of five thousand people was a great honor. It was also work of real service to a people so greatly oppressed by the white man's government in South Africa.

Every day there would be people he could help. As a child, he had often opened the door of his uncle's house before dawn to see patient people waiting with stories to tell their chief—people turned out of their homes by the white man's laws and prevented from settling anywhere else by another law; men whose children were hungry and who were denied work by the government; people who could not leave to take work in a nearby city without a pass and yet had been denied a pass for one reason or another; others who were forced to remain in the terribly overcrowded settlements because the black people of South Africa were not allowed to live where white men lived or gathered for business. These were the problems of his people, so they were his problems, too. How could he help them?

As he clasped and unclasped his hands, Albert Luthuli heard the college choir rehearsing in another room. Even in the midst of his thinking, his heart lifted as he heard the young voices. They were singing a song he had taught them— a song with special meaning for Luthuli and his people—"Let My People Go." The young people were singing it as *he* had taught them to sing it, he realized joyfully. Yes, these African students were also his people.

On the following day, he asked for leave to go to the mission reserve at Groutville to visit his family. His wife and children were living in that village with his widowed mother.

He could not make his decision without first discussing it with Nokukhanya, for he valued her judgment and strong Christian faith.

Minutes after he had arrived and greeted his family he was pouring out the story to Nokukhanya. "We would be together more often," he said. "But the chief's salary is small, and we have the children to think about. It would be a harder life for you and the family."

"That is not so important," said Nokukhanya quietly. "What is important is that you should be happy in your work. You have enjoyed your life at Adams, because you feel that the students need you. I feel this, too. You are a teacher at heart, and you must think of all the young people who are your students."

"Why?" ask Luthuli. "Just because they need to learn language and music, and how to run and manage a school?"

"No," answered his wife, smiling, "you know that is not the reason. It is because they are young, and open to new ideas. They are studying to be teachers. We must depend upon our teachers to help the cause of all our people."

And so it was decided. It meant parting again from his wife and children, for his mother could not be left alone on the reserve, but he returned to Adams College with his mind made up to continue teaching.

The years there passed swiftly, but happily. Meanwhile, the laws against the black people grew worse. Although there were ten million non-whites in South Africa, the government felt it was responsible only to the three million white people of the country. For years it had refused to grant any kind of equality to the majority of the people—the Negroes, the Indians, and "the Coloreds," who were part white. The government passed laws that were part of a definite plan to keep whites and non-whites apart. This plan for complete segregation gave the white people all the best land for lovely parks and homes, for swimming pools and club houses, while it crowded ten million non-whites onto sandy, poor soil. The black people could not produce enough food for one million, let alone for ten times that number, who were forced to live on the reserves.

Meanwhile, the people of Umvoti Reserve had not given up at Luthuli's first refusal to be their chief.

"Please," the leaders urged once more, "change your mind and come back to us."

Still later they said, "Conditions on the reserve grow worse without good leadership. We fear for the welfare of the tribe."

Their messages and pleas were disturbing to Albert Luthuli. As he walked about on the quiet campus at Adams College, he knew that although he had once said, "No," he had never been satisfied with his decision. He had been educated in a Christian school, and his life had been constantly dedicated to the Christian ideals of love and service. Was God speaking to him? Did his restlessness mean that God was telling him, Albert John Luthuli, that his place was with his people in Groutville?

Walking alone one quiet night under a black velvet sky and low-hanging stars, Luthuli came to a new decision. Filled with a deep sense of inner peace, he planned how he would tell Nokukhanya. She would understand, he knew, just as she always had. But he was not prepared for the letter that awaited him when he returned to his room—a letter from Nokukhanya saying that she had changed her mind, too. She now thought he should leave Adams and come home to be the chief of his tribe! Surely God had spoken.

In the years that followed on the Umvoti Reserve, Chief Luthuli heard the age-old story of poverty, sickness, hunger, and need repeated day after day. Always he did what he could to help. He taught his people better ways of growing food, better care of children. Sometimes he traveled away from the Umvoti Reserve to consult with chiefs of other tribes. He found that it was the same story everywhere: Negroes were living with neither dignity nor justice, nor a ray of hope for a better tomorrow.

Again and again Luthuli tried to reach the leaders of the South African government, to tell them of the desperate plight of his people. But always he was refused permission to write or talk to the officials. At last he decided that an end to the injustices could come only if his people acted together, and spoke with the voice of a united group. So he organized the African National Congress and helped to draw up a Freedom Charter, using the Bill of Rights of the United States Constitution as a pattern. Then he traveled all over the country talking about the Freedom Charter, and the need for all Africans to support the leaders of the new Congress.

"But what good will this do?" the younger, impatient men asked him. "There has been too much talking!" Luthuli knew that this was true, but he could only answer, "There are people beyond South Africa who sometimes hear what we say. All we can do is to try to shout to the world." Albert Luthuli did his best to help his people shout loud enough for the world to hear.

Chief Luthuli made it clear that the freedom and justice he sought was not for non-whites alone. He wanted to see a South Africa where all people, white or colored, of any creed or religion, could live and work together in peace. The idea grew. Thousands of people gathered whenever Luthuli was to make a speech. And the flame of social justice, feeble at first, grew to a steady glow as the years went by.

Soon the officials found that Luthuli had attracted many white people to his cause of justice and equality. One day when Chief Luthuli had attended a meeting of the South Africa Parliament, he stood in a hallway talking with a reporter. Suddenly a young white African rushed up to him and gripped his hand, an action almost unheard of between whites and blacks in South Africa.

"I am ashamed of my people!" he said. "I'm ashamed of what's going on in that meeting!" And he was gone before Luthuli could answer.

This was what the government most feared—sympathy for

the condition of the non-whites. Immediately they moved to stop what they called "treason." They issued orders that Luthuli might not travel to large cities, and followed this with even stricter orders that he must not go more than twenty miles from home. He was first forbidden to speak at any meetings, and later forbidden to talk to more than one person at a time.

But these actions failed to stop the demands for freedom, so the government accused Luthuli and the people who were working with him, both black and white, of high treason, and put them on trial for their lives.

At four o'clock one December morning the police knocked on the door of Luthuli's home to inform him that he was under arrest. Two policemen stayed with him as he dressed, while two others were charged with keeping watch over the rest of the house.

"Will there be time for breakfast?" asked Nokukhanya.

"Oh, yes," responded one of the men. "We will have to search all his papers before we leave."

The treason trial drew the attention of all the world to South Africa. What had been only a national problem now became of world importance. Albert Luthuli, who had been a leader known only to his own people, now became an international figure. Gifts of money from freedom-loving people from all nations poured in, to hire the best lawyers to defend the prisoner. By their efforts Luthuli was acquitted of the charges.

His release from prison brought a feeling of joy and victory to the entire world.

South African leaders soon recognized that their nation was now in a most unpopular position, and they blamed Luthuli. To punish him still more, to silence him once and forever, they extended his "house arrest" for five years. He was not to be allowed to speak to more than one person at a time for five years! By tapping his telephone, reading his mail, and examining all his visitors, they made quite sure that the world would hear no more of Albert Luthuli.

But one day a messenger hurried along the dusty unpaved street, carrying a long envelope in his hand. The house he was seeking was a small white home of concrete with a tin roof, the work of the owner's own hands.

"Chief Luthuli! Chief Luthuli!" called the messenger breathlessly. "Where is the chief?"

The serene African woman who answered the door looked quietly at the excited young man. "You'll find him where he always is at this time of day, working in his cane field," she replied, pointing the way. And she returned to her housework, not even asking the reason for the excitement.

But in the lot stood the rugged chief. A sturdy man with a massive head and close-cropped hair now nearly all gray, he was singing under his breath as he cut the sugar cane. Even in undertone the richness of his bass voice could not be disguised, and seemed to add a feeling of sadness to the old folk song:

Where are we Africans?
We seem to be nowhere.
We shall wander and wander and wander.
How far shall we go?

"Chief! Chief!" shouted the messenger. "Read this! The Norwegian government has announced that it is going to award you the Nobel Peace Prize, one of the greatest honors in the world!"

The chief stood with the telegram in his hand. That he was pleased showed in his wide, happy smile. He turned to the messenger. "This is indeed an honor, Tembo. But not for me only. It honors every African who has helped me in our long fight for freedom." And as he turned toward the house, to share the news with Nokukhanya, he murmured, "And we haven't won it yet—not yet."

Stories of great men should have triumphant endings. But the end of Chief Luthuli's story is not yet in sight. His house arrest has been extended for another five years, and the bans on him have been made stricter. As before, no one is allowed to visit him without government permission. But in addition, he is not permitted to go to the nearby town of Stanger, or even to attend church. Meanwhile, the laws against the ten million black South Africans are growing more and more oppressive.

What will be the outcome? Chief Luthuli writes in his biography, *Let My People Go:*

The task is not finished. South Africa is not yet a home for all her sons and daughters. . . . The struggle must go on. . . . The struggle will go on. . . . *Mayibuye iAfrika! Come, Africa, come!*[1]

Responsibility for answering this call lies not only with Africans but with Christians everywhere.

QUESTIONS

1. Go to your school or public library and do some research on Chief Luthuli's life, including the most up-to-date information on his house arrest. Prepare an objective, factual report to present orally for group discussion.

2. Read Jesus' "Great Commission" in your Bible (Matthew 28:19-20) and tell how this relates to Chief Luthuli's life and work.

[1] Albert Luthuli, *Let My People Go*. New York, McGraw-Hill, 1962. Pages 231-232. Used by permission.

9   A Teacher Plus

PETER B. WRIGHT, Jr.

"I can't stress it too much, men. TNT, or any high explosive for that matter, is deadly. You have volunteered for the most dangerous job in the army. The day you forget the danger, that day you are lost!"

Peter Wright looked out of the window and tried to hide a yawn. "Teachers keep saying the same thing over and over again," he said to himself. "If I ever go into teaching, I won't bore my students as this guy is doing."

Suddenly he felt a jab. "Hey, Pete." It was his buddy whispering urgently. "Don't go to sleep in class; you'll get extra K.P. duty. For Pete's sake, wake up." Then he looked at Pete, "And don't forget; it could be *for Pete's sake* that you should listen!"

Pete grinned. But the room was hot. He thought of the spring training days on the football field. He had loved his days as an end on the Clemson College team.

Pete Wright, tall, broad-shouldered, was a man of action. Now undergoing training in demolitions, he realized that he had to listen to as many lectures in the Army as he had at college. What was the instructor saying? "It's field work next week, men. You'll all have actual explosives to handle. Remember," he gave the men a wry smile, "the life you save may be your own!"

Pete's first field assignment was more to his liking than listening to lectures. He went over his instructions carefully. "Remember, Wright, however careful you are, don't forget that you are doing deadly work. Take care!" It was the instructor's voice as he walked from group to group.

That was the last sound Pete remembered for a long time. Later, his buddies told him that the TNT exploded with a noise like the crack of doom. And he lay unconscious on the ground.

Now it was weeks later and he was lying in the darkness in the quiet hospital. He had vague remembrances of people coming and going. Sometimes he felt that all that was left of Pete Wright was one vast never-ending headache! The hospital was so quiet, so quiet. Suddenly in that lonely room, Pete Wright panicked. For in that terrible moment, he realized that the silence was not in the hospital, it was in Pete Wright. He was deaf!

Silent days passed, relieved only by a muffled sound of voices which he could not understand. Two words only seemed to be drumming in his ears, or written in flame before his bandaged eyes, "What now? What now?"—two words burned into his consciousness by the explosion of half a pound of TNT.

What to do? Before, he had only to decide among the many possible answers. A football career? His coach thought that he had a future in athletics. Whether to play, to "turn professional," to coach, to teach athletics—the only difficulty was to make a choice.

Other times at Clemson he had thought that perhaps teaching was his calling. He felt happiest when he was teaching—a church school, a tennis club, a group of students.

"Mom, what do you think?" he used to ask. "Should I go out for football? Or would you rather have me be a teacher?"

But quiet-voiced Mrs. Wright would look at her tall young son and shake her head, "Just be the best that you can. That is all I ask. Ditch-digger, football player, coach, teacher . . . just be the best that you can!"

In the silent darkness of the long hospital night, Pete could hear her voice as clearly as he had heard it so often at home.

"Be the best, Son. You can serve others in whatever you do."
The best? The best what? Bum? Beggar? What does a person
do who cannot hear and who is not yet trained to do anything?

The doctors had the answer to that. First, they declared
him well. Then he grew strong enough for training—slow,
wearying training. Watching the lips of the instructor, he
spent hour after hour trying to learn what was being said.
Being fitted with a hearing aid almost drove him mad because it brought to him a wild jumble of noises, impossible to
sort out, making his head ache beyond endurance.

"What now, Mom? What now?" he would cry out and her
answer was always the same, "Have faith, Pete. God needs you
to work for him. Be the best that you can! The best that you
can!"

So he went back to watching the instructor mouth words
slowly, writing them down—twenty mistakes, ten mistakes,
two mistakes; practicing every day with the hearing aid—a few
minutes, half an hour, an hour.

And all the time the doctors kept saying, "You are the same,
Peter. You can do whatever you planned to do before. You
can see what we are saying. You're good, Pete, you're getting
better."

So there came a day when Peter Wright was discharged
from the hospital, fitted with a hearing aid, equipped to read
lips as quickly and as accurately as once he had heard sounds.

"Go on with whatever you had planned, Pete. You can!

You can! Be the best! Be the best!" This was the inspiration his mother had given him.

Pete decided to finish college, to go on, to train as a teacher. Days of lectures, of note-taking, were commonplace now at Newberry College. He scarcely thought of his inability to hear. If his eyes watched people's lips and his head turned from speaker to speaker, it was not even noticeable, so skilled had he become.

And with this skill, Pete's life became as normal and ordinary as any young American's. He married a pretty girl, and had a lovely family. He accepted a position teaching senior high science, and he became his pastor's assistant at church. He loved to teach tennis to his children, take them on church outings. Days weren't long enough to do all he planned. When school was over, he taught adults at night. He became the head of the adult education work in Bartow, Florida.

It was on one of these rushed busy days that Pete, riding the quiet roads that led from Bartow to his school, saw something that he had passed a hundred times and never before had noticed—a gang of men working to repair the road. They were men from the prison camps of Florida, a common sight.

Day after day the prisoners labored under the hot sun. At evening time they were marched back to the prison camp where the steel gates closed behind them. Suddenly, as if for the first time, Pete Wright saw them not as a group of prisoners, but as people, people with human needs.

"Hi!" he would say, and his wide friendly grin could not

be ignored. "How's everything with you?" He would have short conversations with them as he passed going back and forth to school. Sometimes he would ask a casual question, "Where did you go to school?"

Little by little he began to know them, the young men who had not finished school, who through misfortune or wrong-doing had landed in jail. When they had finished their prison terms, all too often they could not get good jobs, because they had had so little schooling. Money would be scarce, and they would lose hope. Soon they would be in trouble again—and back in prison.

Peter Wright saw a need and wanted to do something. He sat in the office of Mr. Dozier, his principal. "Why couldn't they have adult classes, just as the people in Bartow do? Why couldn't I teach them in the prison camp? If they could get through high school, they could hold better jobs when they were released."

"You could try it!" was Mr. Dozier's response.

So Peter did! But not with official encouragement. The prison boards thought the idea was foolish. "Do you really think that after those fellows have worked all day on the road-mending detail, they are going to want to go to school at night? You're crazy!" a board member said.

"I can tell you now, Mr. Wright," said the warden. "Those guards work long hours now. You don't order them to over-time duty you know!"

Peter Wright grinned to himself as he came away from one

such conference. Mother had told him to "be the best." At least, she would have to admit that he was becoming the best pest the prison officials had ever known!

But he wore them down, and finally won the right to hold classes in the Bartow Prison Camp twice a week. The warden may have secretly thought that the teacher would tire of the whole business and everyone would have peace at last! But he didn't know Peter Wright.

In March, 1956, Pete held his first class. By 1963, Pete had seen thirty-one classes start in the various prison camps of the state of Florida. Nine of them he had started himself.

Two nights a week Pete would rush away from the supper table, kiss his wife Betty, wave to his four youngsters, and hail the armed guards at the prison gates, where he was admitted. The boys would come into class, clean and shining in their pale blue slacks and open-neck shirts. No one would ever have guessed how they had sweated all day long on the roads.

Each boy had his own work. Quietly they would go to the cupboard and take out their textbooks and their workbooks. Peter and his helpers would move from table to table, correcting some spelling here, marking some math there. One evening as Pete passed down the long cafeteria table, one older man furiously chewing his pencil looked up from his workbook. "English!" he groaned. "Whoever invented the stuff?" Pete smiled at him, looked over his exercises. "Why, you're doing just fine, Tom," he said.

As in day school, there were tests, exams, and assignments.

If Peter ever tired of marking papers for twenty to thirty grown-ups at night after he had taught all day in school, he never let the men guess it. And if the men ever felt so tired after a hard day of back-breaking toil that they wanted to skip school, they never told him so. Teacher and students worked towards the day, the wonderful day, when the warden would give them the high school diploma they had earned.

But to be the best kind of teacher, as Peter Wright knew, you must know your students and be interested in every one of them. Soon he found that besides the four hours of class-work and the hours of marking papers, he was spending up to ten extra hours with the prisoners. It all had begun when Joe, one of the best of the students, didn't come to class.

"Where's Joe tonight?" Pete had asked the men. But they just shrugged their shoulders.

Another night and no Joe. Two weeks went by. Pete felt he must do something. He skipped supper that night and went early to the camp.

"Joe," he said to the sullen-looking boy lying on his berth, "what's happened to you? I've missed you from class!"

"Heck! Who cares about school? It's just baloney!" the boy said.

Pete sat beside him quietly. He asked a few questions. He cared. It was too much for the unhappy prisoner. Finally he broke down and shared his troubles with Pete. Things were wrong at home. His wife was finding it too hard without his earnings. He wanted to go home but he still had months to serve. "There's nothing I can do," he said thickly. "I can't stand it. I think I'll go mad. I keep trying to plan how to break out." His voice was hard. "But I'd only get shot at the gates."

Peter Wright laid his hand lightly on the arm of the prisoner. "Ever tried praying, Joe? It helps." There was something in the quiet assurance of his voice that made Joe look. Although he didn't know it, Pete was putting into those words all the heartbreaking hours of hopelessness in the dark nights in the hospital room, all the weary hours of trying to read the silent words, all the impossibility of enduring the noise of the hearing aid—and all of his faith in God's love. He knew an answer and Joe recognized it.

So Peter Wright became a "teacher *plus*." He taught as all good teachers do, but he also spent hours with the men before and after classes, listening to the men, counseling them, writing home for them, and praying with them.

When the men graduated, they returned to the outside world. With a high school diploma, they found better jobs, and fewer and fewer of them returned to prison. But they were often lonely when they went out. They needed help, they needed a friend. To his teaching and counseling, Pete Wright added another piece of service. He wrote to the boys.

When he was asked about it, he grinned and replied in his soft Southern accent, "I write about six or seven letters a week. The boys need the encouragement. They plan on hearing from me every month."

As Pete worked with the men in the camps, he learned more and more that their great danger was to forget what the outside world was like; to think of themselves only as prisoners; to forget that once again they would be men when their term was over.

"They need to do things all the rest of us do, Olen!" Pete said one day to Mr. Raiford, who worked with him. They need to go to church, for instance."

Olen raised his eyebrows. It was useless to say to Peter Wright that this was impossible. Pete knew no such word!

And so Pete added a Sunday to the days he spent with the boys in prison. He took them to church, Sunday by Sunday, without guards, without weapons.

It was a guard who had rebelled against the extra hours he had to be on duty while the men were in classes, who really summed up the whole matter. He looked down the scrubbed cafeteria tables, at the blue-clad prisoners bent over their battered-up textbooks, and he looked at Mike typing like mad at an old discarded typewriter—Mike, by the way, being one who had college in his after-prison plans. Then, before the guard spoke, his glance followed the tall lithe figure of Peter Wright moving from student to student.

"You're asking me about Mr. Wright?" He turned to the new prisoner beside him, "All I can say is, he's the best, *the very best.*"

QUESTIONS

1. Why is it important for a prisoner in a prison camp to earn a high school diploma before he goes out to get a job and lead a normal life again?

2. If you were a member of the church to which Peter Wright took prisoners every Sunday, how would you welcome them?

10   A Worldwide Stage

CHARLES MALIK

It was the day of the voting in the General Assembly of the United Nations. Silently a tall husky man entered the tension-filled Assembly room and took his place. To have Charles Habib Malik, an Arabic-speaking Lebanese, running for president against an Arab from the Sudan was unheard of. Would the delegates remember the things Dr. Malik had stood for—human rights, equality, justice? Would they remember his courage in saying what he thought? His fairness?

The room grew quiet as the secretary began the roll call. In alphabetical order, the countries of the world represented in this great Assembly cast their votes. Some voted for Dr. Malik, some against. All the while, Dr. Malik sat with his head in his hands; but from the excited buzzing in the room he knew that the vote was close.

At that time there were only eighty-two countries in the UN. Would there be a majority of those voting who believed in the cause of unity? A majority who wanted peace instead of power? A majority who hoped for the rights of man—the Declaration of Human Rights? These were long, tense moments; and in flashes that took him back to his home in Lebanon, Dr. Malik had time to remember how it all happened, how he happened to be sitting in this vast Assembly room waiting for the long roll call of nations.

Born to a doctor's family in the tiny country of Lebanon, Charles Habib Malik did not seem likely to become a world statesman. Yet in his small country, neighboring nations could never be forgotten. People from many parts of the world coming to see the famous Cedars of Lebanon; statesmen representing many nations; traders and ships from every country—all were familiar sights to any Lebanese boy.

But little Charles was not concerned with such weighty matters as world statesmanship as he played gaily with his friends. In the cool evenings he challenged his buddies to a game of hopscotch—*afreet*, he called it—or joined the rest of the children in another lively game. Then he ran home to a cool drink of *leben*, waiting for him in his mother's kitchen. Sometimes when he came home from school he snatched a few freshly baked *mankushis*. Charles thought that no one made them quite so light and melt-in-your-mouth as his mother and grandmother. Then, too, there were always oranges and grapes, or dried figs and walnuts to tuck into the hungry corners every growing boy has.

Doctor Habib Malik and his wife were Christians, so it was natural that they should send their son to Christian schools. The standards of the American Mission School were high, and often the work seemed very hard. Yet Charles really enjoyed learning about distant places and their peoples. He loved to read stories about famous men—adventurers, kings, explorers, and heroes of all lands. He was one of the best students of his class, mostly because he was so eager to learn and understand new ideas.

Among these new ideas were some that were to become very important to him. He had a favorite teacher who often brought him books to read. This teacher was a Christian missionary.

"Why do Americans care so much about other countries?" he asked her one day. "Why do they give away so much money?"

"We are not here because we are Americans, but because we are Christians," she answered. "We are here because Jesus taught us to love our neighbors as ourselves."

Charles also made friends with the boys from many other

faiths who lived in Lebanon. He had many Muslim friends. In his relations with them he was never bashful or apologetic about his Christian faith or his religious convictions.

All too soon, school days in the small Christian school were over. When he finished high school, Charles entered the American University at Beirut. By this time he had learned to read and speak both Arabic and English, which helped him to study the writings of great scholars in philosophy, the subject he loved most. Charles, it was clear, was mainly interested in people and what they thought about.

One day Charles rushed to his classroom early and pressed a large book into the professor's hands. "Look, sir," he said excitedly, "look at this book my friend gave me!"

The professor smiled. It was good to see a young student become so excited over a book. "Why, that's Dr. Whitehead's book, *Science and the Modern World*," he said. "Tell me, why did you find it so interesting?"

Charles's words came out with a rush. "Dr. Whitehead explains so many things about today's world that I never knew before. And he has given me so much to think about! He must be a wonderful man!"

"Dr. Whitehead is a professor at Harvard University, in the United States," replied the teacher. "And he is, indeed, a wonderful man."

"Well, this book has helped me make up my mind about what I want to do after I finish here," said Charles with a smile. "Maybe I can earn a scholarship that will help me go to Harvard and meet this Dr. Whitehead—and perhaps even study with him."

"I'm afraid our scholarships aren't big enough for that, Charles," his professor told him. "But I'm sure you could go to the United States and study at some smaller school, where the expenses would not be so heavy."

"If I go to the United States, I will go to Harvard," stated Charles firmly. "If the scholarship isn't enough, I'll earn the money myself."

And so he did. One of his ways of earning money was to stop smoking cigarettes. And in three years he saved enough from this abstinence to pay his boat fare to New York. From there he made his way to Harvard University, and immediately registered for Dr. Whitehead's graduate course.

During his years at Harvard he gained the respect of both faculty and students, not only for his scholarship, but also for his ability to express himself clearly and simply.

"Charles," said one of his friends jokingly, "you talk exactly like a teacher. You always explain what you mean, first, second, and third, even in everyday conversation!"

People found, too, that he was fair in his judgments. He seldom got angry with people who disagreed with him; he was never afraid to say exactly what he thought, or to point out where someone might be wrong. And so it was that when he finished his courses and was called Dr. Malik, he returned to Beirut to teach philosophy at the American University of Beirut.

He taught philosophy at the university for eight years, and became head of the department there. During this time, Lebanon won her independence. In 1945 the government of the newly independent country asked Dr. Malik to serve as the Lebanese representative to the United Nations. Dr. Malik did not want to leave university life, for he was deeply interested in his students and his books, but his government insisted that they wanted him for this important post.

Finally he accepted and asked the university for a leave of absence for one year. Bayard Dodge, who was then president of the university, said to him, "We can give you this leave, if you're sure it is what you want, but I believe you will be happy to get back here with us. You'll find that the business of persuading all the nations of the world to get along together is pretty confusing and discouraging!"

"I'm sure that that's true," answered Dr. Malik. "But this may be the place where I can best serve my country in these crucial days. I must not refuse to be of service if I am needed, but a year passes quickly—and I'll be back before very long."

How little he dreamed that "before very long" would mean exactly a decade! For this was the time when the United Nations was setting about to write a document for all governments to live by. It was later to be called the Declaration of Human Rights. It was important because it set forth the basic needs of every human being—a home, a job, privacy, dignity, happiness, among others. Dr. Malik wanted to have a part in writing this document, and wanted all the world to read it and have the same faith in human beings and human rights.

But as Dr. Malik continued his work with the United Nations and the Declaration of Human Rights, he remembered the words of President Dodge—"confusing and discouraging." Some peoples wanted more power, some were afraid of other larger countries, some wanted to get even with their enemies, and some, like North Americans, had forgotten their ideals and were far too concerned with *things*.

Over and over Dr. Malik spoke to small groups of businessmen about it. "What will you do," he asked them, "when you have supplied the people of the world with all the gadgets they can use? Will that be the end of your business?" He remembered Dr. Whitehead and went on to answer his own question. "Your business as Americans is to export to every country your sense of justice and your hopes for independence for all peoples. You must give the world some ideals to live by, and not just *things* to live with! America must export ideals, as well as tractors and refrigerators!"

But Dr. Malik knew that his speeches were not reaching enough people. He felt, too, that if his ideas were to be useful, they must be supported by the United Nations. He was President for one year of the Security Council, the part of the United Nations that deals with military conflicts around the world, and there he kept reminding the nations to live up to the Declaration of Human Rights.

Finally the chance he had been hoping for came. He was

nominated for President of the General Assembly. If he were elected, he would preside over all the countries in the UN, and he would have a worldwide stage from which to speak. His opponent was Sir Leslie Monroe of New Zealand.

Dr. Malik knew that he was sure to be elected if he made a point of the fact that he was Arabic speaking, for he would have the support of the African, Asian, and Middle Eastern nations. But this meant seeking the support of Asia and Africa against the Western countries—dividing the world into two groups, one set against the other. And so, because he wanted unity and brotherhood more than the highest office in the UN, Dr. Malik withdrew his name as a candidate, and Sir Leslie Monroe was elected.

When some of his friends objected to his withdrawal, he told them, "Do you not see that East and West must share the work of the world together?" But they did not see, and they could not know how hard it was for him to lose the election and his chance for a worldwide stage for promoting human rights.

Dr. Malik was nominated again for the presidency the following year. But by then the situation had changed, and an Arab from the Sudan ran against him. Thus, with a Lebanese running against a Sudanese, both from countries belonging to the League of Arab States, Charles Malik could put his ideals of faith and justice to the test because only the countries of the Middle East would be divided, not the whole world. Some Middle Eastern countries might vote against him, but there might be some who agreed with what he believed. If he were elected, he could give his message to all the world: that you should treat every person in the human family with respect; that no one can make you a slave; that you have the right to free elections, to home and food and education. Although he talked to many people before the election, no one could give him any assurance as to how the voting would go.

And now, would he lose the presidency again because of his ideals? He lifted his head from his hands as the secretary stood up to announce the result of the vote.

"Dr. Malik—forty-five; Mr. Mahjoub—thirty-one." The room broke into an uproar before the secretary could finish the sentence. But Dr. Malik was silent. Humbly he was thinking of the doctor's son from a remote village in the mountains of northern Lebanon and his Christian home. Now he had won his worldwide stage!

QUESTIONS

1. Do you think Dr. Malik was influenced by his Christian faith when he withdrew his name from the nomination for President of the UN General Assembly?

2. Go to the UN section of the library and read some of Dr. Malik's speeches, after he became President of the General Assembly. Select some parts of the speeches which show what he did after he won his worldwide stage! How do these reflect his Christian faith?

11 Homemakers

CURTIS and MARY MURRAY

"The day camp seems deserted, Ma." Curtis Murray was looking out the window down the grass slope. "No one is on the dock, no one in the boat, no one swimming. A bit unusual for this time of the morning."

Mary Murray put the freshly baked cookies on the cooling rack and joined her husband. "Today's the last day," she said wonderingly. "The teachers and counselors will surely be disappointed if the attendance is down the last day."

Just then a knock sounded, and Mrs. Murray looked over at the glass kitchen door. "I wonder who that can be. I can't see anyone."

"Open it, Ma. It's always a good way to find out," Mr. Murray said teasingly. Mary opened the door and there stood a very small boy and girl. Solemnly they held out a gaily crayoned card.

"Look, Curtis," Mary exclaimed as she read the card.

"Please come to our sharing program. Today at 10 A.M. Big Barn. Gaines-Carlton Larger Parish Day Camp."

Mary stooped until her snow white hair was on a level with the blond curls and the dark curly hair before her. "Tell teacher we'll be there." She smiled. "And now, how about a cookie each, just out of the oven?"

But in a sudden fit of shyness, the little girl shook her head, clutched the little boy's hand, and away they sped down the flower-lined path.

Mr. and Mrs. Murray followed them down to the barn— their own barn, now changed into a craft center and class-rooms, and complete with a puppet theater. Sometimes Mr. Murray couldn't help thinking of the fine milking cows that he had housed there in former days.

"It's far more valuable now than it was then, though," Mr. Murray said to himself.

As the Murrays opened the door, they stood completely amazed. No wonder they had seen no children swimming or playing outside! The barn was full of children and parents. And the moment the Murrays appeared, a voice shouted, "Here they are!" and everyone started singing:

> For they are jolly good fellows,
> For they are jolly good fellows,
> For they are jolly good fellows,
> Which nobody can deny!

During the clapping that followed, two primary children led the smiling couple to two chairs at the front. They were somewhat embarrassed as they sat down. Two kindergarteners were waiting with leis of flowers to hang around their necks. Mrs. Murray noted with a fleeting gleam of amusement that someone had been busy in *her* flower garden!

Then the show began! The window beside the closed curtains of the puppet theater opened and the little clown's head—the one Mary Murray had helped the children make at last year's camp—greeted them:

"Good morning, everyone! Welcome to the sharing session of the Gaines-Carlton Larger Parish Day Camp. We in the junior department are bringing you a play which we have written and produced ourselves. It is called, 'The Life of Mr. and Mrs. Curtis Murray.' We made the marionettes and we are working them ourselves."

The announcer quickly swallowed a giggle, shifted from one foot to the other, then continued: "Any likeness between the puppets and any people here is purely co- co- (here there was an audible prompting)—incidental." Giggles could be heard from the back of the stage, followed by a group, "Sh-h-h-h-."

The announcer's head disappeared from sight as a sturdy little puppet glided into a room where a tall white-haired lady puppet was sitting by a table. "Ma, we will be picking apples today," the sturdy man puppet said. "How many do you want brought up to the house?" The tall puppet got up jerkily from her seat and said, "Bring up two bushels, please, Curtis. I like to have enough pies frozen for people who need them."

The curtain fell as the announcer's head appeared again. "This could be called the story of the Murrays' life. Pies, cookies, butter, cream, eggs. Whatever they had on the farm was valuable to them only if it helped somebody else who was in need. Look, Mrs. Murray has a visitor."

As the curtains opened, a tall man puppet came in. "Good morning, Mary. I just stopped in to thank you and Curtis for the apples and squash you left on our porch. You shouldn't be so generous. You'll be bankrupt. I know you were just as generous to all the other ministers who have been in the parish."

"Mr. Beech," said Mary puppet, "you work so hard helping all of us. It's little enough we can do for you."

Curtain.

The announcer went on with the story: "Mrs. Murray found time in these days to start her doll hospital. Once when she was a little girl, her favorite doll was broken and there was no place to go to mend it. Mary promised herself that when she grew up she would learn to mend dolls so that no little girl would ever have to throw away her favorite doll. She read a lot of books and experimented with broken dolls. Soon people came from all over this area to have their dolls fixed at her doll hospital."

The curtains parted. Mary puppet was sitting with a tiny doll in front of her. A knock at the door sounded and a man puppet came in. "Good morning, Mrs. Murray. I am from the Buffalo Museum. I have brought this doll to be repaired. The doll is worth $200. We have seen your work and feel that you can do it. Could you put aside your work and do it right away? We need it for a display next week."

Mary puppet looked up. "I'll be glad to help you. But first I must finish this doll."

The man puppet sputtered, "But that's a very commonplace doll!"

Mary puppet said firmly, "No doll is commonplace when it is loved by a little girl, as this one is."

Curtain.

The announcer went on with his story: "Three children grew up on this farm. They remember days filled with picnics, bird walks, homemade bread, and many other good things. But all the days here at the Murray farm were not good. Listen!"

Again the curtains parted. Curtis puppet was jerkily moving from side to side of the stage. "I don't care what the doctor said, Mary. I don't know anything else but farming. I can't give it up. My heart can't be that bad. What would we do for money?" Mary puppet walked over and put her hand on Curtis puppet's arm.

"Curtis, we need you. The grandchildren are growing up. Let's sell the farm. You told us God would take over when we don't know what to do next. Something will open up for us."

Curtis puppet spoke slowly. "You are right, Mary. Why am I fussing like this? I have you and the children and the grandchildren. I can still keep our lovely flower gardens. I will have more time to help in the church. I will telephone about selling the farm right now."

The announcer continued: "The farm was sold except for eight acres, the house, and the barns. To the Murrays' surprise, they did not have time to miss the farm. You are going to see a meeting of the Larger Parish Council."

As the curtains parted this time, the puppets were sitting around a table. One fat lady puppet started to speak. "We must find some other place for our church vacation school. When the children go from building to building—as they have to do because our church school is overcrowded—they run the risk of auto accidents. Many people feel that our children should not cross the road. So last year we had vacation church school at the Fish and Game Club, but that is not available this year. What shall we do?"

"Let's give up our vacation school. Lots of other churches

have." Strange—the older man puppet with a white beard had the voice of a very young girl.

"We have well over 150 children every year. It is the best Christian education our children could possibly have." It was the minister puppet speaking. He waved his arms and sounded very convincing.

"We'll have to give it up. There's nothing else to do."

Then Curtis puppet stood up. "Yes, there is. We'll plan to have it on our eight acres. I know the young people and children will help." Then he added with a smile, "And it will keep me out of mischief."

The announcer continued: "When we had day camp that next summer, we found that Mr. Murray had widened a stream to make a swimming pool and a boating pond. The pig pen had been cleaned up and moved on to a foundation to make us a cabin. We all helped bring stones for our fireplace. Mr. Murray helped us plant the trees so we could have a worship park. We think we have the best park for a day camp of any church in America!"

The announcer's head disappeared from his window, the curtains were drawn, and there was an expectant silence in the barn.

Suddenly a very familiar shock of dark red hair appeared around the curtain, followed by the freckled face of the Murrays' grandson, Mickey. Self-consciously he straightened his wrinkled jeans and brushed down his red shirt. Then, in a squeaking voice that gradually grew stronger he said, "Grandpa

and Grandma, our discovery group here was studying about
people like Dr. Verghese and Chief Luthuli. And then we
talked about why they were great. At first we thought it was
because they were famous, like Dr. Malik, or won a Nobel
Prize, like Chief Luthuli. Then our group discussed it some
more and came to the conclusion that these people weren't
great because of what they *did* but because of what they *were*.
They lived their Christian love and faith every day. So we
think you are like them. You gave us this camp, and helped
folks whenever you could, and then you had us. . . ."

The shout of laughter from the audience completely con-
fused the blushing Mickey. Helplessly he stood in front of
them all. Suddenly the face of Mickey's younger brother,
Roger, showed around the corner. "Give them the badge,
dopey!"

A look of relief came over Mickey's face as he jumped from
the stage, landing right at the feet of his smiling grandparents.
Then he put a crayoned badge in the Murrays' hands and disappeared through a side door in the midst of shouts and applause.

The badge read, "WE LOVE YOU." As the Murrays stood up
and turned to face the cheering audience, it was hard for them
to see clearly because their eyes seemed a little misty.

But every time they looked down at the barn in the years
to come, they would remember that beautiful summer morning and a crayoned badge that read, "WE LOVE YOU."

QUESTIONS

1. Try to name some people in your community who have shown their Christian love in much the same way as the Murrays.

2. Turn to the New Testament in your Bible and find examples from the life of Jesus that show his compassion and love for others.

A WORD ABOUT THE FORMAT

Type: Electra 11 point leaded 4 points

Composition, printing, and binding: Sowers Printing
Company, Lebanon, Pa.

Paper covers: Affiliated Lithographers, Inc.
New York, N. Y.

Text paper: S. D. Warren's Olde Style Wove

Typographic design: Margery W. Smith

936   F.W.